Spirit
Led
Eating

Spirit *Led* Eating

Eight Rules that Lead to Freedom

Erling "Len" Fredrickson, MSW

Pleasant Word

Packaged by Pleasant Word, PO Box 428, Enumclaw, WA 98022. The views expressed or implied in this work do not necessarily reflect those of Pleasant Word. The author(s) is ultimately responsible for the design, content and editorial accuracy of this work.

Unless otherwise noted, all Scriptures are taken from the Holy Bible, New International Version, Copyright © 1973, 1978, 1984 by the International Bible Society. Used by permission of Zondervan Publishing House. The "niv" and "New International Version" trademarks are registered in the United States Patent and Trademark Office by International Bible Society.

Scripture references marked kjv are taken from the King James Version of the Bible.

Scripture references marked nasb are taken from the New American Standard Bible, © 1960, 1963, 1968, 1971, 1972, 1973, 1975, 1977 by The Lockman Foundation. Used by permission.

Scripture references marked msg are taken from *The Message* by Eugene H. Peterson, copyright © 1993, 1994, 1995, 1996. 2000, 2001, 2002. Used by permission of NavPress Publishing Group. All rights reserved.

Scripture references marked amp are taken from The Amplified® Bible, Copyright © 1954, 1958, 1962, 1964, 1965, 1987 by The Lockman Foundation. Used by permission.

ISBN 1-4141-0300-X
Library of Congress Catalog Card Number: 2004097309

In sharing stories from other people's lives in this book, some names and details were changed to protect their privacy.

This book is not intended to provide therapy, counseling, treatment and clinical advice, or to take the place of clinical treatment from a professional mental health provider or personal physician. Readers are advised to consult qualified healthcare professionals regarding mental, emotional, and medical issues. Neither the publisher nor author assumes any responsibility for any possible consequences from any reader's action or application of information in this book.

Dedication

For Laura,
a woman of endurance and hope

Table of Contents

Acknowledgments

I am grateful to the many people who made this work a reality—some of whom will never understand the full impact they had on this journey.

My friend, and the catalyst for this book, Robert Grant was a constant stream of support and encouragement.

My mentor and friend, Pastor Ken Jumper, taught me a great deal about the reality of God's presence in my life. His teaching fanned into flame the belief that God can use one person's story of victory for the benefit of many.

The committed and gifted staff and Board of Directors of The Renewal Center in Lexington, SC stood by me as I juggled the demands of serving my clients, writing, and providing leadership to the ministry.

Abbi Phillips is a natural-born cheerleader who helped polish this work through her expert copyediting.

Introduction

Several times a week, for the past several months, many people have asked me the same question: "How much weight have you lost?" My answer is always the same: "I don't know." People are not sure what to make of that answer, because I have obviously lost a lot of weight; there is "less of me to love." They are unaccustomed to someone not keeping meticulous track of their weight loss and not wanting to shout their losses from the mountaintops.

After this initial question, other questions usually follow and our conversations go something like this:

"You don't know how much weight you've lost?"

"Nope."

"What are you doing? Which diet are you on?"

"I'm not on a diet."

"Are you exercising more?"

"Not really."

"So it's like a 'food is fuel' thing. You only eat when you're hungry."

"No, because food is more than fuel."

"You only eat until your full?"

"Not always."

(Getting agitated) "*THEN WHAT ARE YOU DOING?!*"

In a single word, the answer to that question is "*obedience.*" Not obedience to a diet, an exercise regimen, or my body, but obedience to God and what His Word tells us about food. This book will help you discover what went wrong in your relationship with food. It will also help you renew your relationship with God so that He can more actively guide you on a day-to-day basis. You will learn how to hear His voice in these matters like never before.

I find myself responding this way to people when they ask about my weight because I discovered early in this journey that *Spirit Led Eating* couldn't be explained in five minutes. It is markedly different than anything most people have heard of or experienced before. It took me over two years to get these truths through my thick skull! Though many of us have searched for answers in diets, exercise, and other means of weight loss, the truths contained in these pages have been available to us since the beginning of time. We have simply overlooked or ignored them.

It is true that my obedience to God has led to blessing and I have lost a significant amount of weight since I began applying the eight rules for *Spirit Led Eating*, and I'm not the only one. However, *Spirit Led Eating* is not about losing weight. That was not my goal nor should it be yours. So I can't guarantee that you will become thin by applying these truths. But I am quite certain that you can be free like you have never been free before!

I strongly encourage you to read the entire book carefully and thoughtfully. This is especially true because I don't share how to prepare for and fully integrate *Spirit Led Eat-*

ing into your life until the last chapter. As you read, share your thoughts and observations with your spouse or a close friend. Start writing a journal. Enjoy the journey.

It is my prayer that God will meet you in a new and special way through this book. I believe you will experience freedom and peace in the area of eating. May He bless you and your family like never before.

CHAPTER 1

Finding Freedom

So if the Son sets you free, you will be free indeed.
—John 8:36

Ask a Fat Person

As a professional social worker that counsels people, I'm required to attend continuing education training on a regular basis. Several years ago I attended one such training. As I was getting settled in my seat before the seminar began, the instructors walked in. One of them was a very large woman, obese by anyone's standards. Although dressed professionally, she wore her dress like a tent and her legs appeared puffy and tired from the weight they bore.

This woman was an expert in her field. She had helped hundreds of people in her area of specialty and I had a lot to learn from her. Yet, as she began her introduction of the course, she decided to talk about something completely unexpected. It was a subject that was probably on the minds of all the participants—but no one would have dared to comment about: her weight. This gifted professional may have learned that people tended to focus on her size instead of the subject at hand and perhaps she thought it was best to address the issue of her appearance at the outset of the training.

She began to speak to our training group and said something like this: "If you want to know how to lose weight, *ask a fat person*. People who are as overweight as I am know how to lose the weight. We try every diet that comes out only to lose weight and gain back more than when we started. I have lost hundreds of pounds over the course of my lifetime and have gained it all back and more. Fat people are not undisciplined or lazy; they work very hard at losing weight. I *know* how to lose weight.

"After realizing I was fighting a losing battle, I decided to simply give up. I came to believe it was more unhealthy for me to suffer, lose weight, and gain it back than it was to just to accept my situation and myself." After she made this statement, she proceeded to skillfully instruct us in what we had come there to learn.

Of all the things said during the course of that seminar, the one sentence that had the most impact, the one sentence that has haunted me since, was her brilliant observation: "If you want to know how to lose weight, ask a fat person." I believe this statement is a profound truth.

The Merry-go-Round

If you are reading this book, you or someone you love is either overweight or struggles with their relationship with food even if no one else knows. Like me, you have lowered the amounts of carbohydrates you eat and increased your protein intake. You have eaten all the carbohydrates you wanted and cut out fat. You have been on diets only consisting of exact balances between carbohydrates, protein, and fat. You have eaten only vegetables. You have suffered through liquid diets. You have taken medications to decrease your appetite or to make you feel more full. You have resorted to eating nothing for long periods of time. You have spent hundreds of dollars and hours consulting with professionals. You have read EVERY book written on the subject of diet and weight loss and have applied their teachings. You have watched hours of workout videos, joined several health clubs, and bought exercise machines (now coated with dust or sold at the last yard sale). You have attended support groups with others like you. You may have even had surgery to force you to eat less.

I have attempted to lose weight since I was thirteen years old. I was always successful to a point and for a time. My cousin is a wonderful woman and honest to a fault. Once, at a family function, she made the observation (in front of others, to my shame!) "Yeah, you lose a bunch of weight, and gain it all back again, lose weight and gain it back . . . it's what you do." I wish I had accepted the wisdom in those words instead of becoming angry (and not expressing it). I would have saved others and myself years of pain. I was stuck on the weight loss/weight gain merry-go-round. I was going up, down, and around; up, down, and around.

I'm not a doctor or a dietician but in all of my experience I have concluded that there is only one way to lose weight. You have to decrease the amount of calories you take in and/or increase the amount of calories you burn. You must burn more than you ingest and then you lose weight. Graphically it looks like this:

If calories taken in are < calories burned, then weight will decrease.

If calories taken in are > calories burned, then weight will increase.

Sounds simple, doesn't it?

More Than Physical

But you and I know that the physical part of weight loss is only part of the equation. There is more, much more, to it. If you are like me, food does not just feed you physically. Until rather recently, when I was sad or anxious, I wanted to eat. I pursued a feeling of fullness to compensate for *any* emptiness I felt inside. My world revolved around food. It became my comforter, my secret friend, my source of pleasure and joy. I could always turn to food when I felt everything and everyone else was against me.

The sad part is, during most of the years of my struggle I was a Christian. I had access to a loving God who said He "came to seek and save that which was lost" (Luke 19:10). As far as my relationship with food was concerned, I at first didn't know I needed rescuing.

Later I learned that I *did* need rescuing but I didn't want to be rescued—I didn't want to give up what food *did for me*. In effect, I was saying to God, I will love you and serve you and give you my life . . . just not this one part of my life. Like a woman who stays in a relationship with an abusive boyfriend, I couldn't fathom the idea of my life without my relationship with food.

Statistics show that obesity is rampant in Western society. A report published by the U.S. Centers for Disease Control[1] states:

"In 2000, the prevalence of obesity among U.S. adults was 19.8 percent, which reflects a 61 percent increase since 1991. In 2000, 38.8 million American adults met the classification of obesity, defined as having a body mass index, BMI score of 30 or more. Between 2000 and 2001 obesity prevalence climbed from 19.8 percent of American adults to 20.9 percent of American adults. Currently, more than 44 million Americans are considered obese by BMI index; that is, have a Body Mass Index (Kg/m²) greater than or equal to 30. *This reflects an increase of 74 percent since 1991"* (italics added).

One would think that the Christian church would be more conscious of this trend and respond accordingly. Unfortunately one research study[2] reported that obesity is more prevalent in the Christian church than it is among people of other faiths. I have never heard anyone in the church speak out about obesity or gluttony. I have heard sermons about sexual purity, refraining from gambling, the perils of drinking and drugs, but none about overeating. In fact, if you attend a church function, observe that there is always too much food for people to eat. We seem to encourage each other to overeat!

Painful Stereotypes

Yet there is also an unspoken resentment in the church and in society towards overweight people. Having been thin many times in my life, I know that people treated me differently when I was large. My job options were sometimes limited. Before marriage, some girls wouldn't date me. Clerks at stores were ruder to me. My opinions were not as well respected and some ministry doors were closed.

I used to take these reactions, these judgmental attitudes of others, very personally and would use them as an excuse to go on eating binges. I would become angry and resentful toward their negative stereotypes and their discounting of me simply because I was overweight. Like many overweight people, I was often hypersensitive to criticism. Some of you reading this book may even be feeling anger at these words as you read them. I have now come to accept why others sometimes respond to overweight people in a negative manner. What makes people who struggle with overeating different from people who struggle with other defects of character is that we, literally, wear the weight of our sin for all to see.

In Nathaniel Hawthorne's classic, *The Scarlet Letter*, Hester Pryne is forced to wear a large, red "A" on her garments signifying that she is guilty of adultery. Imagine for a moment that you are responsible for hiring people where you work and are conducting interviews. An interviewee walks into your office with a big letter "L" on his chest. Pretend that you know that this 'L' means he struggles with telling lies. So as you are interviewing him, even though you don't say anything about the 'L,' your opinion of him is impacted by what you infer about his character based on the letter he wears. We who struggle with overeating wear our own scarlet letters for all to see. We may be saddened and embarrassed but should not be shocked by the judgmental attitudes of others.

It is Not about Dieting

This book is not a diet book. There are no recipes, no exercise plans or weight loss charts in the appendix. I will not write a companion book with any of those things present. There won't be a line of *Spirit Led Eating* snack foods.

This book was born out of a personal journey that started three years ago. By that time, I had been on the weight gain/weight loss merry-go-round for twenty-four years—almost two-thirds of my life. I finally decided I was going to do battle with this monster, this dragon in my life, and slay it, or die trying. I was tired of fighting losing battles and was determined to win the war.

The first step was to realize that over the course of my life I had made food a god. I was like the Old Testament kingdom of Judah: I said the Lord was my God, but I didn't tear down all the "high places" set apart for other gods. My relationship with God was primary but it was not the only relationship I gave myself to. I will explain in the next chapter how this happened in my life and provide you with a tool to help you discover how it may have happened in your life.

The next step in my journey was to accept the fact that my eating habits were completely out of control. I had to admit to myself that sometimes I did "crazy" things to maintain my relationship with food. For instance, I would sneakily eat two or three extra scoops of ice cream before bringing my overloaded bowl to join the rest of the family in order to make them think I wasn't eating as much. I would stay up much later than I ought just so I could eat anything I wanted to and be alone while doing it.

In every sense of the word, food was an addiction. The problem was, unlike an alcoholic or a drug addict, I could not abstain completely from eating. We must all eat to live. Yet I knew I couldn't trust myself to monitor my own intake of food over a long period of time—I had tried that before several times and failed.

The third step was to realize that I could not conquer this alone. Several years ago, I joined a for-profit weight-loss center. During an appointment with my "counselor" (I never saw any credentials), I told her that I thought there might be an emotional connection to my eating. She looked at me like I had two heads and she never replied to my statement!

Later, I attempted to get involved with support groups but found that many of the people there were focused only on losing weight and not interested in addressing the underlying emotional and spiritual connections they had with food. Also, many of the people I met there were experiencing tremendous emotional upheaval in other areas of their lives. I felt out of control, yet my life was well ordered in comparison to many of theirs. Still later, I tried to get the support and encouragement of friends and from my wife, but they couldn't fully understand my plight. I was also determined not to make them responsible for my overeating.

The last step was the most important: I turned my focus completely toward God. I prayed:

> "Lord, this life I live is not what you intended. The way I think about and use food is not honoring to you. The answer to my problem has not been found in diets, exercising, or relationships with others. But I know you know the answer Lord. Please reveal it to me so that I can be free. Please reveal it to me so that I can honor you like I never have before."

The events that followed unfolded rather quickly. I took all the lessons I had been learning about overeating and condensed them into a few simple guidelines that would help me as I daily applied what God revealed to me. Simultaneously, and most importantly, I began to research the Bible and read every scripture I could find about food and man's relationship with it. God has a lot to say about food in His Word.

I then took my guidelines and compared them with scripture to be sure that my thoughts were correct. I found that some of my guidelines, forged by what the experts and common wisdom said about food, were false and had no Biblical justification. These guidelines were either abandoned or altered dramatically.

I also found that my guidelines were incomplete. Through scripture, God revealed other truths about man's relationship with food that I had never heard or read or thought about before. I was able to take all of these truths and to classify them into eight broad categories. I then made them applicable by turning them into eight personal rules, what I call rules for *Spirit Led Eating*.

I believe these are indeed rules and not guidelines. You can draw outside of guidelines. Those of us who have been on the dieting merry-go-round are experts at finding loopholes in dieting guidelines. In following rules there is safety. If I obey the speed limit of 45 miles per hour on the road near my home, I am protected from a possible accident due to the curves of the road and the level of traffic. I am also protected from the consequences of breaking the rule, such as receiving a speeding ticket.

We who have been on the merry-go-round are much better at following rules than guidelines anyway. For a time, we can endure near starvation. We are capable of following a recipe to the minutest detail. We can be very disciplined!

I believe that these rules are not my own, they were created by God and have been available to us since time began. We have chosen to ignore them. Many people, including my wonderful wife Laura, have always applied these rules in their daily life without giving them a second thought. This is why, for a very long time, she couldn't understand why I struggled the way I did.

The evening I put these rules on paper, I was very excited about sharing them with Laura. My wife is a very honest person and I knew that if I had gone off track (or off my rocker), she would be the first one to tell me so. But as I shared them with her, I found myself weeping. I could barely get the words

23

out! It was then that I realized I was on the right track. I had found God's way toward freedom from overeating.

In all of my attempts to lose weight I was successful . . . temporarily. I dieted and/or exercised, lost weight, but gained it back with more to boot. I got sick of the physical and emotional ups and downs. At times I gave up and gave in. But instead of giving up permanently, I made the decision to give it up to God and sought Him believing that He knew how to free me. He responded by putting me on a path to freedom.

I invite you to ask God to open your eyes, your heart, and your mind to these truths. I know from my own experience the embarrassment and shame you feel from all the failed attempts and the way others have treated you. The Lord says to you today,

"Arise, my darling, my beautiful one, and come with me. See! The winter is past; the rains are over and gone. Flowers appear on the earth; the season of singing has come, the cooing of doves is heard in our land" (Song of Solomon 2:10b–12).

It is time to be free. It is my prayer that you will have the courage to face yourself, trust Him, and start to live the life He has always intended for you.

Endnote

[1]CDC. (2003). *1991–2001 Prevalence of obesity among U.S. adults, by characteristics.* Retrieved from: http://www.cdc.gov/nccdphp/dnpa/obesity/trend/prev_char.htm

[2]Ferraro, Kenneth. 1998. Firm believers? Religion, body weight, and well-being." *Review of Religious Research* 39:224–244

CHAPTER 2

It's All About Relationship

Spirit Led Eating: Rule Number 1

**I will seek God's will for my life every day—
I will put food in its rightful place.**

"Jesus answered, "It is written: 'Man does not live on bread alone.'"

—Luke 4:4

"For the kingdom of God is not a matter of eating and drinking, but of righteousness, peace and joy in the Holy Spirit,"

—Romans 14:17

Spirit Led Eating centers on the idea that if we struggle with overeating we need to experience a drastic change in our relationship with God. For you, this may mean you have to seek Him and trust Him in ways that are foreign to you at present. By living out this rule, you will learn that He is trustworthy and cares deeply

27

about helping you find the answer to this problem. He will begin to show you how to overcome.

It also means that your relationship with food, as you now know it, must end. In the last chapter, I used the analogy of our relationship with food being like a woman involved with an abusive boyfriend. Not every moment of such a relationship is painful; there are times of relative calm and false "peace." However, the long-term price for continuing in an abusive relationship will be increasing violence and possible death. So it is best for the relationship to end and the woman to free herself from further harm. This is also true of our abusive relationship with food.

How the Relationship Manifests Itself

A good friend of mine, who struggled as I did and has been freed by *Spirit Led Eating*, shared this story with me. My friend's in-laws were visiting his family. During the course of their visit, they had mentioned casually that they wanted to take his family out for dinner prior to their leaving. That casual comment became his focus for their visit. On the day before their departure, he thought: "Tonight is the night! We're going out to eat!" Early in the morning, he began to pester his wife about where they were going out to eat, when they were leaving, etc. He was obsessed about it. He wanted to visualize the menu, begin to plan all he was going to eat, and imagine how he would feel afterward. That evening meal became the focus of his day while his wife and in-laws wondered what in the world the big deal was.

When he was finished with his story, my friend thought I would laugh at him or would think he was out of his mind but, on the contrary, I completely understood. I, too, had planned days around my eating, even structuring events to steer myself and my family toward what or where we

28

would eat. If I had to go away on a business trip, I would fantasize for days or weeks about a favorite restaurant in that area. And if I had an expense account—I could eat what I wanted and not even pay for it! Special occasions and holiday meals were not events for me anymore. The *food* at the events *was* the event.

I am sure many of you reading these pages, if you are honest, can remember the times you have made food the center of your day or the center of your life. Some people secretly hoard or hide food so they can eat it alone. Others "treat" themselves to secret snacks throughout the day. Our stories illustrate that those of us who overeat have an inappropriate relationship with food.

Where the Relationship Turned Sour

I do believe that some people have a genetic predisposition or hormonal imbalances that contribute to their being more overweight than others. I also believe that most of us (including me) are overweight because of our own choices. We were not created to have an inappropriate relationship with food.

Young children seem to have an innate ability to moderate food consumption. If you have ever woken up with a newborn for a two o'clock feeding then you know babies *demand* to eat when they're hungry. When their hunger is sated, they quit eating. Toddlers are aware of when they need to eat and tend only to eat to the point of feeling satisfied.

These natural controls are often replaced as children age. How many of us were told as children to finish every morsel we were served, to 'clean our plates,' or to remember all those "starving in India?" Although God instills in children a natural eating equilibrium, we are thrown off

29

balance by the lessons of our parents and others. We are taught to overeat.

In my early childhood, I was a skinny kid. (I toyed with the idea of including a particularly embarrassing picture of my four-year-old self in a bathing suit as proof, but vetoed the idea.) Throughout most of elementary school I was an average sized boy. But in late childhood and in early adolescence, my eating habits changed. My friends even noticed my preoccupation with food and commented on it. As I gained weight, other children in the neighborhood, my friends, and my family teased me mercilessly. Into my adult years, people continued to comment about my weight. I know that my eating habits broke my wife's heart many times by making her watch me grow . . . and shrink; grow . . . and shrink; and grow, and grow, and grow.

Even though I was bombarded by emotional darts from without and within about my eating and my weight, I was not deterred from pursuing a relationship with food. *I just wanted to lose the weight.*

Can you see the distinction? I didn't want to change what food did *for* me; I just wanted to change the *consequences* of my inappropriate relationship with food. When I realized this fact, when I finally saw the insanity of the merry-go-round, I decided to get off. I began to ponder the causes and I asked myself several questions: What happened? What led to the change in eating habits? Why did I tenaciously hold on to the way I related to food for so long despite the shame and embarrassment of being overweight? I have come to believe that the answers to these questions, for me and for you, can be found in two places: our reactions to problems in our families of origin and a choice that we made and continue to make until being set free by God Himself.

My family

I am the youngest of five children and the only boy. My Mom jokingly calls me "Finally" Fredrickson because my parents had hoped for a boy each time they had a baby. Just when they had accepted the idea that they were only going to be blessed with girls, Tada! I showed up. I have been late for things ever since . . . but I'll have to cover that in another book.

My parents deeply loved each other throughout their marriage. My father died in 1984. According to what I have heard from others my father and mother were both extremely attractive and sweet people in their early marriage.

My father taught me by example the importance of honesty, that hard work of any kind is good work, and that taking time for your children is necessary. Dad taught me to laugh at life and at myself.

My mother remains one of the smartest people I know. Although in her seventies and armed with only a high school diploma, she can beat me at Scrabble. She is one of the most giving people I have ever met. I learned how to sacrifice, endure hardship, and be adaptable to any situation from her. I am truly grateful that God made me their child.

But there was a dark side to our family. My father was a salesman for several years and as a result, he would often go on business lunches and dinners, which always involved heavy drinking. My father, however, could not quit after the meal and continued to drink. My mother, in an effort to maintain a relationship with him, began to drink as well. They both used alcohol to cover their pain like I used food to cover mine. When they drank they would lose control, becoming very loud and very mean to each other and to their children.

Saturday mornings were the only consistent and truly peaceful time for me during those years. My parents and sisters slept in and I would get up early and turn on the TV. I would still be reeling from the night before, remembering the yelling and traumatized by any violence that erupted or had threatened to erupt. From my point of view there was no one to give me comfort, *so I chose to comfort myself.*

Every Saturday, I would get a HUGE bowl of cereal. If it didn't have sugar in it already, I would add a ton. I would then get a full sixteen-ounce bottle of cola (I can still remember the feeling of the cold glass in my hands). If we had sweet rolls or donuts in the house, I would grab a couple of them. I would bring the food and the drink with me into the living room and park myself on our couch in front of the television. And all by myself, I would laugh at the cartoons as I filled my stomach and my heart with the food I had procured. No one in my family ever commented on my eating habits or inquired about what I did on Saturday mornings. *It was my secret way of taking care of me.*

Your family

I believe you need to identify what went wrong with your eating and when it went wrong in your own life. You may need the assistance of a counselor to help you unravel the core pain that led you to begin overeating.

I have an exercise that may help you begin to see where you went wrong. The diagram below represents the continuum of your life.

Birth 5 10 15 20 25 30 35 40 45 50 55+

1. Make a slash mark (/) on the line above your present age.

2. Thinking back through your life from birth, put an x at the age you were first aware that you needed or wanted to lose weight. We can deduce that whatever went wrong in your decision making regarding food happened before this time. Look at the length of your struggle. For instance, if you are 35 and you first noticed you had a weight problem at 15, you will have been struggling for 20 years!

3. Below the x on the line, break down your life into 5 year increments. Spend some time and think about your life when you were 0 to 5, 5 to 10, 10 to 15, etc. You may need to take a pad of paper or a journal and write down your thoughts as you recall your eating habits and/or when others started to see there was a problem.

4. Try to pin down how old you were when you began to use food as a way of comforting yourself. Put a circle (O) on the line above that spot.

5. Look at the circle and ask yourself what was happening in your life at the same time you began to establish that wrong relationship with food. Maybe there was a divorce, abuse, or death of a loved one. Again, if thinking about this is too painful or if your

33

memory is blocked, you may need to see a competent professional who can help you work through this part. Ask God to be a "revealer of secret things" (Dan 2:47) in your life. This is the beginning of identifying the primary, underlying pain that led you to medicate yourself with food. You need to enter into this healing to be sure you will stay free of the unhealthy need for food.

My choice

Please don't believe for a moment that I blame my parents for my over-eating. My family history is not an excuse; it serves only as an explanation. The Saturday morning secret feasts began a pattern in my life of reacting to anxiety and pain (especially emotional) by eating food. I learned to trust food over trusting God to meet my needs. This is when food became my god.

Every time I ate to comfort myself I did so of my own free but distorted will. No one has ever pointed a gun at me and said "Eat, or I'll shoot!" I was a volunteer every time I overate.

This is especially true because I had dealt with the emotional scars of my childhood many years ago. I had forgiven my parents, learned from their mistakes, have a wonderful marriage and family, and a fulfilling career. But even after I was healed from past hurt, I made the choice to use food as an emotional crutch.

Your choice

God created humans, men and women, you and me, because He chose to. Because we are His creations, He loves us. Because He wanted us to love Him in return, He gave us free will. You can't know for certain if someone *truly* loves you unless he or she is given the choice *not* to love you.

In our relationship with God, free will is useless if we don't have the liberty to express it through acts of rebellion against His rules and laws. This is what every man and woman has done (except one) since the beginning of time. These acts of rebellion are called sin, which literally means 'to miss the mark.'

Since God loves us, He provided a way, through another act of free will, to receive forgiveness for all of the times we have missed the mark. This way was provided through the birth, life, death, and resurrection of His Son, Jesus Christ. Jesus never missed the mark. He was tempted, to be sure, but He never sinned. His sacrifice, through death on a cross, provided the one and only way for us to re-enter our relationship with God. *"For God so loved the world that he gave his one and only Son, that whoever believes in him shall not perish but have eternal life"* (John 3:16).

In order for you to be able to have true freedom and engage in *Spirit Led Eating*, you must be in right relationship with God. For that to occur, you have to make a *positive* choice. You have to choose to receive Jesus as your Savior (Rescuer, Redeemer) and Lord (Master, Leader, Teacher). Then and only then can you call God your Father. John 1:12 says, talking of Jesus, "Yet to all who received him, to those who believed in his name, he gave the right to become children of God."

Receiving Jesus is as *easy* as uttering a prayer. Receiving Jesus is as *difficult* as surrendering your life. You can enter that relationship with God right now. Say a brief prayer like this:

"God, I need You. I have missed the mark in my life more times than I can remember. I have sinned and this has caused me to be far from You . . . but I want to be near. Thank You for sending Jesus who is the Christ, to die for me. I accept Him into my life and heart. I submit to His Lordship and surrender my life to You through Him. Thank You for loving and accepting me. Amen."

If you said that prayer for the first time . . . welcome home!

The Costs

To those of you who received Him before but have walked, like I did, living in bondage to food while you tried to walk in His grace, there is hope for you too!

There are several costs, however.

1. *Your relationship with food (as you know it) must end; it must die.*
   Colossians 3:3,5 states, *"For you died, and your life is now hidden with Christ in God. Put to death, therefore whatever belongs to your earthly nature . . . which is idolatry."* God never intended for you to overeat or be overweight. You must decide to never use food in an abusive way again. This does not mean that you won't enjoy the food God provides for you; on the contrary, He will make your joy complete! But you will have to say 'Goodbye' to using food as a blanket to cover your emotional pain and anxiety.

2. *You will have to get off the dieting merry-go-round and not climb back on.*
   Remember the last diet that "worked" for you? You probably read a book, applied the principles in the

book, and began to lose weight quickly. You measured the foods you ate and were hyper-vigilant about what you would eat. You thought about when and where you would eat every meal on every day. You probably talked with anyone who would listen about how "great" you were feeling, all you were learning about dieting, and how much weight you had lost. You became a dieting zealot. Sometimes I enjoy eavesdropping on these zealots and marvel. They speak their own "diet jargon" to describe where they are in the process, how much weight they are losing, and how they eat. I know what this is like because I have been a "dieting zealot" many times. I have come to realize that dieting was just an effort to control my relationship with food. Again, I was trying to deal with the consequences of the problem instead of the problem itself. Even if I was eating less and losing weight, I still obsessed about food. Eventually I would give up on the diet and the weight would come back again. It is very much like trimming a weed without pulling out the root. It looks good for a while . . . but it comes back with a vengeance!

Pause from your reading to pull out a coin from your pocket or purse. On one side is "heads." That represents overeating. Now turn the coin over. "Tails" represents dieting. Overeating and dieting are just two sides of the same coin. Both sides of a coin represent the full value of the coin. Both sides of the dieting merry-go-round (overeating and dieting) represent the full value of an inappropriate relationship with food.

37

3. *You will have to accept that Spirit Led Eating has nothing to do with your weight.*
Your primary goal must be maintaining a correct relationship with God. As I write these words, I am still overweight. In fact, I was so ashamed of that, I was determined not to begin writing this book until I was thin! But I realized that just because I literally bear the weight of my past choices doesn't mean I am not forgiven and accepted by God. I want to be thinner for many reasons but my goal is not to *become* thin. My goal is to submit my life completely to God and live in obedience to Him.
I have not weighed or measured myself in months. I will do so only when appropriate, like at a doctor's appointment or physical examination. If you continually watch your weight you can reach only one of three conclusions: you will be losing weight, gaining weight, or staying the same.
If I weigh myself and see that I have lost weight, I will *praise* myself (pride), my diet (my ability to control food), and maybe God ("I know You love me because I am losing weight"). If I gain weight I will *blame* myself (self-pity), my diet (my failure to control food), and definitely God ("I'm trying to follow You and You are not rewarding me. You must hate me!"). If I neither lose nor gain weight, I won't know what to think or will assume the worst and think just like I would if I had gained weight. What a trap we put ourselves in!
God doesn't care as much about how my body looks as He does my inward motivation. *"The Lord does not look at the things man looks at. Man looks at the outward appearance, but the Lord looks at the heart"* (I Sam 16:7). The same is true for you. He wants to

38

heal you and to see you fulfill every purpose He has planned for your life.

Restoring Food to Its Proper Place

The only place to put your inappropriate relationship with food is before God, where it belongs. In Joel 2:25, God says, "*I will restore to you the years that the locust has devoured.*" You must submit your will, your life, and your relationship with food over to God. I want to suggest you say a prayer but I want you to realize with finality that you will be giving up a lot if you pray it. You can start by saying something like this:

"God, I surrender. I have warred against Your will regarding food in my life for a long time. Please forgive me. I give to You, maybe for the first time, my entire self—all that I am. I humbly ask You to take this burden from me and to restore me to wholeness and sanity. Give me the wisdom to know how to eat what You provide for me on a daily basis. Help me to apply these rules. Amen."

Remember that if you prayed that prayer, you have surrendered much. As you obediently restore food to its proper place, you will feel a gap in your life. You will not be applying the salve of fatty or sugary food to your inward pain anymore. Anticipate a season of raw emotions.

You may find yourself crying over little things or overreacting to criticism. This will pass and your emotions will come into balance. Because of this, I would strongly recommend not making any major decisions in your life for the first few weeks. If the emotions become too overwhelming, see your doctor or a good counselor for guidance.

As I said before, I don't know how much I weigh or what my measurements are. Yet, interestingly enough, I have found that since I have been applying these truths, my body is changing. The pants I wore yesterday were so baggy they looked silly. My winter jacket is droopy. Recently, a good friend of mine commented that the shirt I was wearing looked like a "tent" on me.

I believe the Lord wants to restore my body and yours to appear more like He originally intended. I do however, accept the truth that I may have so ravaged my body and produced so many fat cells, that I will never be completely thin again. My underlying motivation is to be obedient to His will.

In the next chapter, you will discover how to know with confidence what God wants you to eat. No matter what, let us agree to live in freedom and accept God's will for our lives everyday. I believe He will be faithful to us all.

CHAPTER 3

Thanksgiving

Spirit Led Eating: Rule Number 2

**I will thank God before eating anything
and will not eat or drink anything
I cannot thank God for.**

*"Taking the five loaves and the two fish and looking up to
heaven, he gave thanks and broke them."*

—Luke 9:16a

*"But the man who has doubts is condemned if he eats, be-
cause his eating is not from faith; and everything that does
not come from faith is sin."*

—Romans 14:23

This rule contains one of the most dramatic shifts
in thinking about food that I have ever experienced. It is both liberating and lovingly inhibiting.

Giving Thanks

Thanking God for the food we eat is fundamental to the Christian life. Christ models thankfulness for God's provision in the verse quoted above and in several other places in the gospels. If I asked most Christians if they are thankful for the food they eat, they would say, "Yes!" If I asked them how God would know they were thankful they would say something like, "I ask the blessing before we eat as a family."

I like to eavesdrop on people's meal prayers as well as their "diet jargon." What I have noticed is that many people don't actually thank God for the food they eat. They thank him for "His bounty" or they ask the Lord to "bless" the food. The word "bless" means to pronounce something as being "good." I bless my son when I tell him how proud I am for a great save he makes as a hockey goalie. I bless my daughter when I tell her how smart she is. So when we ask God to 'bless' our food, are we asking him to make it 'good' or are we sincerely thanking Him that we have food at all? Do we take the time to thank Him for everything He provides?

In Jesus' model prayer found in Matthew 6, He tells us to pray: *"Give us today our daily bread"* (v. 11). Many commentators minimize the food aspect of this verse and concentrate on the correct idea that Jesus was also talking of our need for spiritual food—reading God's Word. However, we can't ignore the fact that He was instructing us to ask for daily sustenance from God.

In Mark 6:8, Jesus sends out the disciples two by two with these instructions: *"Take nothing for the journey except a staff—no bread, no bag, no money in your belts."* One of the many things He was teaching them on these mini-missionary journeys was to be dependent on God for their daily physical needs of food and shelter.

I once had a friend who grew up in a single parent family with many siblings. When he and his brother came home from school, they had a choice to make. They could pick up their guns and head into the woods to hunt or they could grab their fishing poles and try to catch fish. They would stay out until they were successful. If they failed to get a few rabbits, squirrels, or walleye, their family didn't have dinner that night and they all went to bed hungry. My friend's family directly relied upon God's provision of food on a daily basis.

In America, we live in a land flowing with milk and honey . . . as well as hamburgers, candy bars, salads, and sodas. We have many choices of where and what to eat. From my home to my office, I pass by five grocery stores, 15 fast food restaurants, over 20 sit-down restaurants and too many convenience stores to accurately count. With all of these choices, it is very easy for us to take for granted that we have food at all.

Have you ever seen a teenager look in a pantry or cupboard (which is full of food) and lament, "*There's nothing to eat*"? We adults aren't much better. Think about the last time you went out to eat with co-workers or friends. It is very easy to enter into a five- minute conversation where the only topic of discussion is *where* to eat! We have become accustomed to having food easily within our grasp. We take our food for granted.

The first step in applying Rule number 2 is actually thanking God for *everything* you eat. When was the last time you stopped at a gas station, bought a candy bar, paused, and prayed: "Thank you Lord for arranging my schedule, my finances, creating the candy bar factory, and placing this convenience store in my path so that I could be nourished with this candy bar?" This may sound a bit melodramatic but I do believe that thanks are in order in these situations.

What if you relied on hunting deer for your family's sustenance? Think of all the trouble you would have to go through to make certain no one in your home went hungry. When you successfully 'bagged one' I believe your mealtime prayer would go something like this: "Thank you Lord for giving me land to hunt, a good gun, a steady aim, and putting this beautiful buck in my path. Amen . . . Pass the venison!" You would be grateful for His daily provision.

Shortly after I started living out these rules for *Spirit Led Eating*, my family ordered pizza. (At this point I can hear all of the former overeaters saying to themselves, "Pizza! Did he just say pizza?! I can still eat pizza?!" Before picking up the phone for delivery, please read to the end of the chapter.) As we opened up the box and gazed at the pizza, I paused before thanking God. I said to my family, "Look at that pizza. It sure looks great, doesn't it? God just reminded me that there are many families within a five-mile radius of our home that have nothing to eat for supper tonight. We should not feel guilty for what God has provided for us but I think we should pause to remember not only that He has given us food to eat tonight but also that He has decided to bless us with something as delicious as this pizza." We then bowed our heads, thanked Him, and enjoyed our meal together.

Before eating or drinking anything, I thank God for His provision. I believe He has what I call an "optimal" menu for my day. Once I became submitted to Him in my eating and began applying all of the rules, I began looking for how He provided. I once had a meeting at church and had to go directly from work to the meeting with no time to eat. It may not seem miraculous that there was food at a church but I was very grateful to find a meal there. I'll sometimes forget my lunch and someone will call me out of the blue to ask me out to eat. God has even provided me with a wonderful wife who is an amazing cook. She spends a lot of time and energy arranging healthy meals for our family. I still have to make choices but I am always grateful for His basic provision.

Can I Be Thankful?

The second part of this rule states:

"I will not eat or drink anything that I cannot thank God for."

I was at a restaurant a while ago with a good friend of mine. We ordered, began talking and then our food came. We thanked God for the food and before "digging in" I said quietly, "Can I be thankful for all this?" My friend asked me to repeat myself because I said it under my breath. I told him I was asking God if it was all right to eat everything on my plate. Then I reprimanded him for interrupting me when I'm praying! We laughed but I then took the garlic toast and moved it off to the side. God had said *"Not the bread."*

If you met my friend Robert, you would never know that he struggled with overeating. He was stuck in a cycle where he would overeat and either punish himself or compensate for the extra caloric intake by exercising obsessively. He did not enjoy the exercise that much but he felt compelled to pay the penalty for his misdeeds. Robert was in a binge/purge cycle. I jokingly tell people I binged but was too lazy to purge!

Robert and I meet regularly for fellowship and accountability. We share our struggles and our victories. He is a wonderful man of God and a gourmet cook. A few days after God revealed the rules for *Spirit Led Eating* to me and before I could tell him about them, he told me a story and asked me a question.

Robert said that he and his wife were planning to have dinner at a friend's house and he had offered to bring dessert. He decided to make his famous cookie ice cream. His recipe calls for using two of the three rows of cookies in the package for the ice cream. When he made ice cream before he realized his problem with overeating, he would usually eat the third row as he prepared the ice cream (his reward for the "hard work" of making ice cream). But this time he was victorious and put the cookies away and didn't eat any! He was very happy with his decision.

That night, he and his wife enjoyed a wonderful dinner with their friends. When it was time for dessert, Robert ate a small serving of the ice cream he had prepared. He would normally have eaten a large bowl, brought home the leftovers, and finished it off later. This time, he only had a small serving.

After the story came this question: "What are we trying to do here? The books we've read say we have to abstain from eating foods like that. But I really enjoyed it and I can't imagine living my life not being able to eat the things I so enjoy. I felt great about not eating the third row of cookies but am I supposed to feel guilty for eating the serving of ice cream?" Before sharing the Rules with him, I asked him one question: "Can you thank God for the ice cream?"

According to what I read in God's Word, we are free to eat or drink *anything* that we can be thankful for—*anything* that we can eat or drink with a clear conscience. How liberating! Most diet books and programs have regimens delineating what you can and cannot eat. Many food-addiction books and programs are reticent in their belief that we identify our "trigger foods" and abstain from them like an alcoholic must abstain from liquor. I can't find a Biblical justification for this notion. On the contrary, God speaks very clearly that we should be happy with the food He provides. In Acts 10, we read a "food metaphor" that God used to teach the Apostle Peter about ministering to people different than himself.

"About noon the following day as they were on their journey and approaching the city, Peter went up on the roof to pray. He became hungry and wanted something to eat, and while the meal was being prepared, he fell into a trance. He saw heaven opened and something like a large sheet being let down to earth by its four corners. It contained all kinds of four-footed animals, as well as reptiles of the earth and birds of the air. Then a voice told him, "Get up, Peter. Kill and eat."

"Surely not, Lord!" Peter replied. "I have never eaten anything impure or unclean."

The voice spoke to him a second time, "Do not call anything impure that God has made clean."

(vs. 9–15)

Like strict dieting, I believe complete, irrevocable abstinence from certain foods turns our eyes and our heart away from God and back on food. It is part of the other side of the overeating coin. It is also ineffective in controlling our out-of-control appetites. We are told in Scripture:

"Since you died with Christ to the basic principles of this world, why, as though you still belonged to it, do you submit to its rules: "Do not handle! Do not taste! Do not touch!"? These are all destined to perish with use, because they are based on human commands and teachings. Such

regulations indeed have an appearance of wisdom, with their self-imposed worship, their false humility and their harsh treatment of the body, but they lack any value in restraining sensual indulgence."

(Colossians 2:20–23)

If you are on a strict diet due to a medical problem like heart disease or diabetes, please don't take God's Word or my words as a license to violate what is best for you. If your doctor told you to limit fatty foods in order to save your life, then please don't believe that you will be able to thank God for those foods. You must submit to the authority of the one (doctor, dietician, etc.) sent to care for you.

I eat any food I can be thankful for but I do not eat every food I want or drink every liquid I desire. Caffeine is a very potent drug and I admit that I have struggled with using it since childhood. My son once said he believed I couldn't stop drinking soda. I proved him wrong by not drinking any soda for an entire year . . . but I didn't quit drinking caffeine. I just switched my method of ingestion to coffee and iced tea. The Lord has made it very clear to me that I can rarely, if ever, drink any product with caffeine with gratitude to Him. It is not His will for me because I use it to keep me awake and vigilant instead of relying on Him.

You may feel complete freedom to drink caffeine. If so, may God bless you! But if I have dinner at your house, please put on a pot of 'decaf' for me!

How To Know What You Can Be Thankful For

The title of this book is *Spirit Led Eating*. I have discussed our relationship with God and Jesus Christ but I have not approached the key role of another person in regard to eating, the Holy Spirit.

During Jesus' last days on earth with His disciples He began to reveal His imminent departure. As the reality of this sunk in, the disciples were very worried and didn't understand how they would function without Him. He eased their concern by making them a promise: *"And I will ask the Father, and he will give you another Counselor to be with you forever"* (John 14:16). And who is the Counselor? *"But the Counselor, the Holy Spirit, whom the Father will send in my name, will teach you all things and will remind you of everything I have said to you"* (John 14:26).

Prior to this time, the Holy Spirit was active in the world but His presence was limited to certain people and for a limited time. The Old Testament documents these incidents in the account of the Exodus, the life of King David, and the prophets. What Jesus told His disciples was something radically different from their prior experience. God was going to be available to them all the time through the indwelling Person of the Holy Spirit. In fact, Jesus said this was one of the reasons He had to leave: *"But I tell you the truth: It is for your good that I am going away. Unless I go away, the Counselor will not come to you; but if I go, I will send him to you"* (John 16:7).

Forty days after Christ's ascension, on the day of Pentecost, the Holy Spirit arrived! You can read about His exciting appearance in Acts Chapter 2. All of the believers in Jesus Christ that were present on that day were affected. Since that time, His influence is available to all of us who believe in Him.

I counsel people as a professional. I give them advice and guidance on how they can deal with emotional problems and interpersonal relationships. I care a lot about the people I serve and I do my best to help them improve their lives. If I didn't see people change as a result of my intervention, I would have quit doing what I do a *long* time ago. So if I can help people as a "little-c" counselor, how much better to have THE Counselor help you with your eating?

The word "Counselor" used in the book of John is translated by different versions as the words Comforter (kjv), Helper (nasb), Friend (msg), Intercessor, and Advocate (amp). The Holy Spirit cares deeply about you and your day-to-day choices. Because He lives inside of you, or indwells you, He is constantly available to you. He brings glory to God the Father and Jesus Christ by providing guidance to us. All you have to do is ask Him.

However, the Holy Spirit will not "possess" you. You have to invite Him to be active and heed what He tells you. You must learn to recognize His voice in your heart, mind, and spirit. I haven't met a sane person who believed they had audibly heard the voice of the Holy Spirit, so we shouldn't expect telephone calls or e-mails from Him. We have to pay attention.

In I Kings 19, we read that after a great victory the prophet Elijah became depressed and afraid. He lost sight of God's vision for his life and questioned God's provision for his safety. He was concerned because the 'voices' he heard (King Ahab and Queen Jezebel wanted to kill him) were so loud and so strong Elijah lost heart and direction. As he ran away in his fear and anxiety, God met him and revealed something to Elijah (and to us) about the nature of His voice.

Elijah was hiding in a cave when God spoke to him: *"Go out and stand on the mountain in the presence of the LORD, for the LORD is about to pass by."* *Then a great and powerful wind tore the mountains apart and shattered the rocks before the LORD, but the LORD was not in the wind. After the wind there was an earthquake, but the LORD was not in the earth-*

quake. After the earthquake came a fire, but the LORD was not in the fire. And after the fire came a gentle whisper. When Elijah heard it, he pulled his cloak over his face and went out and stood at the mouth of the cave. Then a voice said to him, "What are you doing here, Elijah?" (vs. 11–13).

What we learn from this is that God's voice is gentle. His voice is very kind and difficult to hear unless you pay attention over the din and howl of the other 'voices' He must contend with for your attention.

If you like watching football on television like I do, you must endure seemingly unending commercials for various products. Many of those commercials will have something to do with products that you can eat or drink. When you drive down the road and see restaurant names or logos you know by association that you can immediately get a burger, fries, drink, and shake. You have probably conditioned your mind and body to crave certain foods at certain times of the day and your body cries out to you if you interfere with the pattern. These voices from outside and within you are very loud, seductive, and powerful.

God's voice through the Holy Spirit is much quieter, calmer, and less urgent. As you tune your heart to hear His voice, and begin to obey what He tells you, you will become increasingly able to distinguish His voice from the others that seek to lead you astray.

After a particularly long and difficult day at work, I arrived home hungry, tired, and weak. So I asked God silently, "What should I eat Lord?" I heard Him tell me: "Have some cottage cheese and crackers." But I knew we were out of cottage cheese and had been for days. I opened the refrigerator and looked at the place we keep cottage cheese *out of obedience to His voice.* There on the shelf (you guessed it) was a new carton of cottage cheese! Without my knowledge, my wife had gone shopping that day and had purchased it. Isn't our God great! He cares about what you and I eat and drink and wants to guide you towards His ideal eating plan for you.

I ask Him to reveal to me what and how much He wants me to eat *before* I start eating, usually as I am putting things on my plate. God and I have very interesting yet silent dialogues. For instance, the other night as I gratefully dished out the cottage cheese He provided by inspiring my wife as she shopped, we had a discussion that went something like this:

> (Putting three scoops in my bowl) "This much Lord?"
> *"No, that's too much . . . take some out."*
> (Putting about a half a scoop back) "This much?"
> *"A liiiiiiiiiittle less."*
> (Putting a tablespoon back) "How about this?"
> *"Great, son. Enjoy it!"*

If you have never struggled with your eating before, a dialogue like this may sound a little crazy. But, if you have ever longed to receive specific instructions when you are at your weakest, like I was the other night, it is an amazing, freeing, and exhilarating experience. He cares that much about you and what you eat and drink!

This puts the issue of the pizza I ordered for my family in perspective. *On that particular day,* I could be thankful for pizza. I also received guidance from my past experiences with dieting to know I should order a very thin crust and that the main ingredients should be freshly cut vegetables. My appetite and the Holy Spirit directed that I only eat two pieces. I felt God's approval through the Holy Spirit for my meal. I was thankful that I had food at all AND I could be thankful for what I ate. How liberating!

I want to recommend another brief prayer before you begin living out the second rule:

"God, You are Amazing! Thank You for creating me and caring for me. Thank You for the food You provide my family and me every day. Thank You for my next meal. Thank You for sending the Holy Spirit, my Counselor, to guide me in how I should live my life. I am sorry for not heeding His voice earlier in regard to food.

Please help me to hear His voice over the noise of this world and my own selfish appetites. I want to eat only what You want me to and I need your Spirit's guidance in making the correct decisions. Amen."

One of the most difficult parts of living out *Spirit Led Eating* is our tendency to be dishonest with ourselves and with others. You will see in the next chapter that God has much to say about our need to be truthful in order to remain free.

CHAPTER 4

Telling the Truth

Spirit Led Eating: Rule Number 3

I will not lie about what or how much I eat.

"The woman Folly is loud; she is undisciplined and without knowledge. She sits at the door of her house, on a seat at the highest point of the city, calling out to those who pass by, who go straight on their way. "Let all who are simple come in here!" she says to those who lack judgment. "Stolen water is sweet; food eaten in secret is delicious!" But little do they know that the dead are there, that her guests are in the depths of the grave."

—Proverbs 9:13–18

"Food gained by fraud tastes sweet to a man, but he ends up with a mouth full of gravel."

—Proverbs 20:17

Please pardon the pun, but this rule may be hard for you to swallow. It's difficult because it requires us to admit to ourselves, to God, and to others what we thought was hidden. People who struggle with overeating almost always minimize what they eat and the impact it has on their lives. I know because I was VERY dishonest about what, how much, when, and where I ate. I lied about how I looked, what I weighed, and my measurements. I lied to myself, to God, to loved ones and complete strangers. This rule states that you have to admit that you are a liar too.

You have probably heard it said, "Denial ain't just a river in Egypt." In fact, denial is a very potent force and one that is often misunderstood. Denial is not just a simple assertion that you don't have a problem. It is much more insidious than that. Denial distorts the lenses you use to view yourself and your problems. It gives you an untruthful view of your relationship with food. Let me share a story that exemplifies how denial worked in my life.

One evening, as I drove home, I began thinking that it would be nice *for my kids* if I stopped at an ice cream shop on the way home and got them a treat. After all, they are such good children and they don't ask for very much. This would be a nice surprise that would bless them. As I prepared to stop at the store, I started planning a menu, "*for my children.*" I thought: "They like those ice cream and candy combinations. But they like different flavors, so I have to get two of them. I don't have to get any for myself." And you know, when you buy the small size it is a poor value and I want to be a good steward of the resources God has given me. But if I got the larger size, they wouldn't be able to finish it and could save it for later. Or maybe . . . they could share some with their humble and lovable father."

I had my turn signal on and was about to pull in and buy the ice cream when I realized what I was doing. *I wanted ice cream.* They hadn't asked for or expected it. *I wanted the candy with the ice cream. I wanted to use it to* feel better. And I was willing to use my children as an excuse to overeat. I was victorious then but I have failed many other times.

The lies that overeaters tell are of four varieties that overlap and intersect with each other: conscious, unconscious, from within, and from without.

Conscious Lies

Conscious lies are those that we tell ourselves and others that we know are lies when we tell them. It is telling your spouse you only ate one piece of cake when you ate all of it. It is telling the Department of Motor Vehicles that you only weigh 120 pounds when you know you really weigh 135.

Telling lies is a slippery, downward slope. We often force ourselves to tell more lies to cover up earlier lies. If you tell your spouse you only ate one piece of cake he may say: "If you only had one piece, what happened to the rest of it?" Your reply would probably be "Uh . . . um . . . I guess the kids might have eaten it. (*Yelling*) You never believe me! You think I'm a pig don't you?"

When we tell conscious lies, we do so because we are afraid of the consequences of the truth. If you were honest about your weight at the DMV, you think the woman at the grocery checkout counter who checks your driver's license when you write out a check may think you're too fat. First of all, we have to realize that most people DON'T CARE how much we weigh or how much we eat; they are too worried about themselves. If they are going to judge us about our weight, they will usually do so by sight, not by what is printed on a piece of paper. In fact, continued denials, especially in the face of facts, make us appear weak.

People lie to their doctors about what they eat because they're afraid to be told they are failing or are worried they will face greater restrictions on their diets. As I said in the first chapter, losing weight on a physical level is as easy as controlling the number of calories you take in and the number of calories you burn. If your doctor has put you on a strict diet and you are still gaining weight . . . he or she KNOWS you are cheating. Lying about it does nothing but lower his or her trust in your word.

Sometimes we lie because we don't want to hurt the feelings of those we love. For example, if your spouse knew you ate an entire cake, it would mean you disappointed him yet again. But we often forget our spouses will be able to figure out our lies anyway as we continue to gain weight. And being lied to hurts worse than almost anything.

Many people who overeat do so when no one is looking. We wait until our children and spouses are asleep and then sneak into the kitchen to take more food. We even try to clean up the evidence before anyone wakes up the next morning, or as we are preparing food, we surreptitiously take extra food.

One of the behaviors that saddens me most is when overweight people only eat healthy foods and drinks in front of others. They often go to great lengths to demonstrate their commitment to dieting and weight loss, making large shows of their low calorie food. But everyone knows that somewhere, at some time, they are eating other foods and in large quantities because they are obviously gaining weight instead of losing it. I have actually heard people like this say: "I don't know why I can't lose weight. This is all I eat," expecting people to believe it. But nobody does; they're just too polite to say anything.

Unconscious Lies

Unconscious lies are lies that are so deeply rooted that we begin to believe them ourselves. Telling lies is habit forming and we can begin to believe our own untruths. If you tell people you only weigh 175 pounds when you know you weigh 200, eventually you will begin to believe you only weigh 175 and will be shocked when a scale reveals the truth. In fact, you may insist there is something wrong with the scale!

Another manifestation of unconscious lies is our body image. Most of us who were on the dieting merry-go-round avoided having pictures taken of us. We say, "No thanks, I'll hold the camera so you guys can be in the shot." In reality we don't want to have to face how we really look so we can avoid having to do anything about it. We will insist on purchasing clothes that are uncomfortable and look ridiculous on us because we can't admit to ourselves that we are suffering consequences from our inappropriate relationship with food.

Do you remember one of the times you took a good, hard look in the mirror and realized you were overweight? Do you remember the horror and anxiety you felt when you finally saw how large you had become? You probably experienced a feeling of hopelessness and despair, as if it had appeared overnight. Yet those around you had seen you gaining weight by watching your clothes get tighter, and your face and body get rounder. They were not surprised, even if you were, because you were lying to yourself. This realization often is the impetus for trying another diet, but this only serves to keep the cycle going.

At times we lie to ourselves that we have eaten at all. I remember once getting a disturbing phone call that left me riddled with anxiety. I hung up the phone and headed for the kitchen where Laura was preparing dinner for our family. I described the call and the feelings I was experiencing in response. After a few minutes, Laura stopped me in mid-sentence and asked, "Do you know your eating?" I paused, looked down in my hands, and to my surprise found a bag of potato chips. I was wolfing them down between sentences. I had entered the kitchen, began talking to my wife, opened the pantry door, pulled out the bag, and started eating . . . AND I DIDN'T REALIZE I WAS DOING IT! What a frightening revelation.

This is not an uncommon occurrence with those who overeat. I have known people who lost track of what they ate and looked down to find an empty ice cream carton in their hands with no recollection of getting or eating any of it! Sometimes people binge to such an extent that they lose consciousness. These lies are horrifying to both those that experience them and those who watch it happen.

Lies from Within

Lies from within are those that speak from deep within your heart. They may be the voices of past hurts that say, "You can never change. You are fat and you always will be fat." These lies discredit the many works Jesus Christ has done in and through you and try to make you despair of improvement.

As you are reading this book you may be thinking something like, "I'm glad this *Spirit Led Eating* thing works for you, but it probably won't work for me." You feel you have tried everything and have never found freedom before and therefore will *never* find complete freedom. You may feel that *Spirit Led Eating* is too easy to be true. These are prime examples of lies from within!

Philippians 1:6 says: *"he who began a good work in you will carry it on to completion until the day of Christ Jesus."* We can all agree that saving you from your sin was a "good work." If you are still in bondage to your relationship with food, God's work is not finished in you yet. Jesus came to set the captive free. If you're in bondage, He's not done with you. According to this verse, He will not give up on you until the end of time! I haven't given up on you. Don't give up on yourself either! Freedom is very close by . . .

Lies from Without

This may come as a shock to you, but there are many interested parties in your life that want you to remain in bondage. Many businesses count on you continuing to overeat. They want to lead you and don't want you to be led by the Spirit. They entice you to 'stupendous-size' your order. Their packaging screams "low fat" when their products have no-fewer calories than the products they are meant to replace.

After I began *Spirit Led Eating*, I only had time to run to a fast-food restaurant for lunch one day. I prayed and asked God what I could be thankful for. I ordered a sandwich and a diet drink. The person behind the counter said, "Would you like fries with that?" I declined because I couldn't be thankful for fries. He persisted, "Are you sure? It will only cost a few cents more and you get a lot more food . . ." I had to say "No" a second time.

Some people in your family may have a vested interest in your current relationship with food. If you are medicating with food, you don't need to express your true feelings about your parent's or spouse's behavior. At present, they don't have to deal with the consequences of you being real. You being overweight may allow others in your family to point the finger at you as the "problem" person so that they won't have attention drawn to their own behavior. If this is happening, it doesn't mean they don't love you. They may have lost hope themselves or don't understand the full impact of what they're doing and saying.

There is a concept we use in counseling called homeostasis (originally a biological term) that refers to the idea that people and family systems resist all change, even positive change. We human beings don't intentionally try to hold ourselves and others back from freedom; we just don't like what is difficult to understand or different from what we're used to. We're creatures of habit and we fear change.

The primary source of lies from without is our greatest Adversary, the Devil. John 8:44 states, *"When he lies, he speaks his native language, for he is a liar and the father of lies."* Satan lies to you and has taught you the lies you tell to yourself.

His desire is to destroy you and keep you in bondage. Satan couldn't get me to succumb to drug and alcohol addiction. He couldn't get me to compulsively use pornography or gamble. But he told me a lie that did work. He said, *"If you eat, you will feel better."* I bought the lie and was in bondage for over twenty-four years.

It is Satan that tells you to eat what you want when no one is looking. He tells you that you can work it off by exercising more. He lies by blinding you to how large you have become. Satan even lies by telling us that we are the only ones that are hurt when we are overweight. We'll tackle that lie in Chapter 7.

How to Stop the Lies

I believe there are several practical steps you can take to stop lying to yourself and others:

1. Admit you are a liar. Ask God to reveal to you all the times you have lied about food in the last week. Then take a piece of paper and write them all down. It will surprise you how often you lie. You may lie about little else but you will find you lie about where, what, when, and how much you eat. When this is done, ask God to forgive you.

   Then go out and confess your lies to those you lied to and ask their forgiveness. When you do so, ask them if they already suspected you had lied. You will learn you haven't been fooling many people.

2. Purpose in your heart to be a truth-teller. Psalm 130:30 says, *"I have chosen the way of truth."* Lying is a choice. Choose to be a person of truth. The Bible states in Proverbs 12:22 that God *"delights in men who are truthful."* I don't know about you but I want God to delight in me.

3. Select one or two people in your life who will be honest with you and hold you accountable for being honest with them and yourself. Ask them to always give you a truthful answer no matter how the truth may hurt. Give them permission to confront you and promise you will be honest with them. Then you must *be* honest with them, even if you worry their opinion of you will change.

4. Avoid eating alone whenever possible, especially when other people are nearby or available to eat with you. Go to bed when the rest of your family goes to bed. Have someone with you as you prepare meals so you will be less tempted to sneak food.

5. Take inventory of yourself from time to time. Look at yourself in the mirror. Remember that *Spirit Led Eating* is not about losing weight. It's about obedience. While you must acknowledge what is wrong about your body, you must also celebrate what is right about it! So don't beat yourself up about your double chin or other secondary symptoms of your overeating. Instead look at what's right with you! *"Finally, brothers, whatever is true, whatever is noble, whatever is right, whatever is pure, whatever is lovely, whatever is admirable—if anything is excellent or praiseworthy—think about such things"* (Philippians 4:8). Look at the beautiful eyes God gave you. Thank Him that you have hair (trust me, you should thank Him for *every* hair on your head.)

6. Be grateful that you're no longer in bondage. Then and only then will you experience true self-acceptance. You won't have to hide by lying anymore. When you take that pressure off of yourself, you may find that God will redeem your reflection. He may begin to restore your physical image as well. You will start to like what you see again.

Now that you know why it's important to remain honest about what you eat and drink, we will begin to explore our (sometimes) negative reactions to the foods God chooses to provide and the consequences of our ingratitude.

CHAPTER 5

Appreciation

Spirit Led Eating: Rule Number 4

I will not complain about the food God provides for me.

". . . they spoke against God and against Moses, and said, "Why have you brought us up out of Egypt to die in the desert? There is no bread! There is no water! And we detest this miserable food!" Then the LORD sent venomous snakes among them; they bit the people and many Israelites died."
—Numbers 21:5–6

"Therefore I tell you, do not worry about your life, what you will eat or drink; or about your body, what you will wear. Is not life more important than food, and the body more important than clothes?"
—Matthew 6:25

My dog Misty is very intelligent but she has a weak stomach. She can't tolerate "people" food. I should say *we, her family,* can't tolerate the gastrointestinal side effects that occur when Misty eats "people" food. Being an intelligent dog, Misty has learned that we don't voluntarily give her table scraps of any kind. She has learned to stakeout the areas where we prepare and eat our meals. Whenever someone drops something, anything, or a morsel of food rolls off of a plate, Misty pounces! And before we can even react to protect her and ourselves from the potential consequences of her appetites, the food is gone. It vanishes forever like mist in the wind.

Many people believe that overweight people, like Misty, are indiscriminate about what they eat. On the contrary, we are very picky about the food we consume. We may eat a lot of what we like, but we only like to eat what pleases our palate. This is why diets are so cumbersome to many of us. They limit our palates. In fact, many diets just give in to this truth by allowing "cheat" days where a dieter can eat anything they desire.

The Provider

One of the many names of God found in the Old Testament is Jehovah Jireh, which literally means *God, our Provider*. As a Christian, I believe that God provides everything that I need. He provided me with a wonderful wife. He provides me with work that allows me to pay for a house, clothing, transportation, and food.

God said to Adam and Eve in the Garden of Eden, "*I give you every seed-bearing plant on the face of the whole earth and every tree that has fruit with seed in it. They will be yours for food*" (Gen 1:29). After the flood in Noah's time, God expanded His provision by stating, "*Everything that lives and moves will be food for you. Just as I gave you the green plants, I now give you everything* (Gen 9:3)." Note that God Himself said that HE provides food for us.

In I Kings 19, we read the prophet Elijah became depressed as he ran from the murderous Queen Jezebel. He asked God to let him die. God responded through provision. In verses 5 and 6 we read, "*All at once an angel touched him and said, 'Get up and eat.' He looked around, and there by his head was a cake of bread baked over hot coals, and a jar of water.*" God provides for us what we need and when we need it.

I once worked with an Asian-immigrant family for several months. As my time with them was about to end, they surprised me with a meal of food from their native country. I was concerned about what they were about to serve me but knew I would offend them if I refused. So I sat down and began eating. The food was different . . . but interesting. In fact, the seasoned beef was particularly good. They brought the food to me in courses and the entire family gathered around as I took a bite to see my reaction. Things were going along quite well until they brought the last course.

A few days before my visit to this family, I had watched a television show about fishing in Europe. Because the streams and ponds there have been so over-fished, the local fish population is quite discerning when it comes to spotting something on a hook. As a result, the locals have developed a strategy that entails using vivid multi-colored maggots on ultra-light tackle.

There set before me, was a bowl of what looked like the maggots I had seen on TV. They were in some kind of warm broth but I was sure they were maggots. I looked at the bowl and then up at the expectant faces of my hosts. I asked them (as pleasantly as I could), "What is it?" They replied in their native tongue, which didn't help me one iota.

I had a decision to make. I could refuse to eat what they provided me or eat it with gratitude. If I refused I would hurt their feelings and insult the sacrifice they had made to prepare what was to them a feast. If I ate the maggots, I would probably live because based on the looks on their faces . . . they thought maggots were delicious! So I picked up my spoon and put some in my mouth. Praise God! It was multi-colored *tapioca pudding.* I didn't have to eat maggots!

We who struggle with an inappropriate relationship with food take God's provision for our daily needs for granted. We often complain about the food that is provided for us or refuse to eat until we can get the foods we crave. By doing so we insult God in the same way I would have insulted that wonderful family who lavished me with their native food. By complaining about the food we eat, we 'spit in God's eye' and say to Him, "What you provide isn't good enough. I deserve something better." We selfishly try to control how and what we are provided by Him.

I provide instruction and training to professionals and para-professionals on a variety of topics related to human development and interaction. After a lunch break during one of these trainings, I noticed that two participants in the training walked back into the room with cups from two different fast-food restaurants. I asked them what the story was behind the two different cups. They replied that they had gone to one restaurant and ordered chicken for lunch. One of them ate her lunch but didn't like the way the chicken tasted. So after they were done at the first restaurant, she asked the person who drove to find a place with better chicken. They found a different franchise and she ordered and ate another entire chicken meal. They told this story very matter-of-factly and acted as if the second lunch was the only one that counted because the first one had not lived up to her expectations.

Consequences of complaining

In Numbers 21:5, we read the key verse of Rule number 4: *"they spoke against God and against Moses, and said, "Why have you brought us up out of Egypt to die in the desert? There is no bread! There is no water! And we detest this miserable food!"*

God had delivered the Israelites from slavery in dramatic fashion (who could forget the parting of the Red Sea?). They began a long walk to the land God had promised their forefathers. What an exciting time!

There were several logistical problems that resulted from their freedom. Can you imagine the food requirements for the estimated 2 million Israelites who were moving across the desert? God knew this would happen and He provided a food called manna for them on a daily basis. The word *manna* literally means "what is it?" because nothing like it had been seen before or has been seen since. It appeared every morning with the dew and the Israelites went out, gathered and consumed it throughout the day. In fact, God provided a double portion on Fridays so the Israelites would have a day of rest on Saturday.

How did the Israelites respond to this miracle? In Numbers 11:4–6 we read, *"The rabble with them began to crave other food, and again the Israelites started wailing and said, 'If only we had meat to eat! We remember the fish we ate in Egypt at no cost-also the cucumbers, melons, leeks, onions and garlic. But now we have lost our appetite; we never see anything but this manna!"* They had obviously forgotten that the food they were provided with was at the cost of their freedom.

God listened to them and provided quail. In fact, quail were stacked three feet in all directions! God was very displeased with their constant grumbling about the quality of

His provision: *"But while the meat was still between their teeth and before it could be consumed, the anger of the LORD burned against the people, and he struck them with a severe plague"* (Numbers 11:33).

In this era of grace we live in today I won't go as far as saying that God will allow you to die because you complain about the food He provides but I do believe there are consequences. I may hurt the feelings of the person who prepared the food for my benefit. I may miss out on a great opportunity to eat something "different . . . but interesting." I miss the opportunity to give God the glory for providing something for my benefit. Ultimately, complaints about simple provision will lead to complaints about complex provision like where you work, where you live, and whom you decide to marry.

One of the primary consequences of our complaining is obesity. We are not grateful for what is provided to us, so we stop on the way home for something more, something that pleases our palate. As a result, we overeat and we gain weight. If you constantly complain about what is set before you, you will never be satisfied and you will eat and eat and eat until your cravings are satisfied.

In chapter three I mentioned that God provided a meal for me at a church meeting when I was running late one day. I failed to tell you the entire story. When I first looked at what was set before me I rejected it. I said to myself, "I don't want this! It smells awful! I'll get something when I get home." I know myself and I would have been ravenous when I arrived home and may have overeaten. But because of this rule, and the potential consequences of my decision, I thanked God for His provision and ate what was set before me. I don't want to offend God by complaining about what He provides for me, nor do I want to incur His wrath by complaining either.

Free from Worry

If I am confident that God has a menu plan for my life, and I trust Him to provide, I don't have to worry. We are told in Matthew 6:25, *"Therefore I tell you, do not worry about your life, what you will eat or drink; or about your body, what you will wear. Is not life more important than food, and the body more important than clothes?"*

When my children were small they were free from worry about if, when, and what they were going to eat on any given day. They trusted that their mother and I would provide for them. That is the attitude we should cultivate in our relationship with God.

In the height of my overeating, I woke up wondering what I was going to have for breakfast, lunch, and dinner. Again, meals were not opportunities to gain nourishment and fellowship with others; they were something that I wanted to maintain control of. Meals were stressful for me, not relaxing.

If we are led by the Spirit, we can be confident that God will meet all of our needs. We don't have to worry or obsess about our daily bread. He's got it under control. Ask Him to help you accept what He provides for you. Ask him to help you not over-think meals. This doesn't mean you can't do meal planning. Simply avoid being so utterly rigid that you're unprepared for a detour from your will from time to time.

The next rule of *Spirit Led Eating* is going to be difficult for many people to accept or understand because it requires that we admit that our overeating often rises to the level of offense against God—that it is sinful.

CHAPTER 6

The Sixth Sin

Spirit Led Eating: Rule Number 5

*I will repent every time I am guilty of gluttony
or obsess about food.*

*"Do not join those who drink too much wine or gorge them-
selves on meat, for drunkards and gluttons become poor,
and drowsiness clothes them in rags."*
—Proverbs 23:21

*"When you sit to dine with a ruler, note well what is before
you, and put a knife to your throat if you are given to gluttony. Do not crave his delicacies, for that food is deceptive."*
—Proverbs 23:1–3

You may have heard of the "Seven Deadly Sins," a list of human behaviors that were, in medieval times, considered the core vices of mankind. During my life as a Christian I have heard many sermons about the evils and perils of Pride, Envy, Anger, Greed, Sloth, and

Lust. I do not, however, recall hearing a sermon about the sin usually listed as the sixth deadly sin: *Gluttony*. Gluttony is a harsh word; it's not pretty or politically correct. It's not a word that is used frequently.

One of the most difficult portions of my journey toward freedom through *Spirit Led Eating* was facing the unpleasant truth that I had been guilty of a horrible sin for many years even after I had received Jesus Christ as Savior and Lord. **I was a glutton.** My character and my body were stained by the fact that I ate and/or drank in excess of what was appropriate or necessary. The fat I wore was a calling card of my sin. And people often treated me accordingly.

Most overweight people can share stories of being misjudged and suffering some form of bias due to their weight and size. A group of health care professionals who participated in one study[1] indicated that they endorse many stereotypes about obese people including that they are "lazy, stupid, and worthless." The most surprising part of this research was that the health care professionals who were studied specialized in working with the obese! This stigmatization is very painful and often unfair, but it is a reality. As discussed in chapter one, we literally bear the weight of our sin.

As I mentioned earlier, almost all of us have lied to cover up our sinful behavior with food. There are gluttons who are so motivated to cover their sin, they resort to punishing themselves by purging via obsessive exercise, using laxatives, or vomiting.[2] Although concealing their sin, they are still committing the sin of gluttony. Even if these people don't appear to be overweight, they are gluttons.

When one is a glutton, it not only reflects your penchant for food, it says volumes about your character—who you are at your very core. No one believes that overweight people are jolly or happy in our culture. People assume

74

you are miserable but don't have the self-respect or self-discipline to do anything about it. Those people either don't understand the nature of habitual sin or they are forgetting about or are covering up their own habitual sin. However, they are correct in their observation that something is amiss—something in your life is not the way it should be.

Jesus Himself was accused of being a glutton (Luke 7:34). This false accusation was used as a way to discredit His ministry. In Shakespeare, we read about a character named Falstaff, a glutton. Although a popular and comedic character, his excessive eating, drinking and being over-weight is considered a major character flaw in the plays he appears in.

Today we are afraid to label gluttony for the sin that it is. One of the reasons for this may be the fear of hurting peoples' feelings. I remember being teased mercilessly by other children as I grew up and how much it pained me because their taunting magnified the shame I already felt because of my weight. As I said earlier, most of us who are overweight are nothing if not sensitive to criticism.

Another reason we minimize the notion that (sometimes) overeating equals gluttony equals sin is because it is acceptable and encouraged by our society. Television commercials are dominated by food and drink manufacturers and retailers. The portions we are served in restaurants are significantly larger than we need or even intend to eat. We are given the double message: "Eat and drink what pleases you in large quantities" *but* "Don't be fat." We can't win if we play by the rules of our culture. We must be careful, however, not to blame others (restaurants, TV ads, etc.) for our decision to sin.

Damage Done by Gluttony

God's Word is wonderful in that it not only corrects us, but it provides explanations as to why a given sin is bad for us. This is true of gluttony. The Bible says, "*Do not join those who drink too much wine or gorge themselves on meat, for drunkards and gluttons become poor, and drowsiness clothes them in rags*" (Proverbs 23:2). Obtaining and using food in a gluttonous way diverts our energies from God's purposes for our lives. God has a plan and purpose for your life. However, if eating and drinking dominate your thoughts and actions, you have little time and energy left over to pursue His will for you.

When I was a glutton, I felt like I was on the sidelines of God's will for my life. Frustrated and working hard in other areas of my life to earn God's favor, I tried to excel in everything I put my hand to. What did not accompany this hard work was the humility to admit or surrender this core sin of gluttony. I believed, as many overweight people do, that excellence in everything else somehow made up for failure to control this one "little" area of life. As a result, I eventually hit a wall where God couldn't use me more until I dealt with this sin. This was a very difficult realization for me to come to. But it was true.

Early in my journey as a Christian, a friend of mine introduced me to Proverbs 23:2. On her refrigerator was an index card that read "*Put a knife to your throat if you are given to gluttony.*" She used it as a way to try to scare herself away from overeating. I remember thinking to myself "Wow! God is tough. We're supposed to kill ourselves instead of eating too much cheesecake?" It sounded like we should behave like Samurai warriors and commit Hari-Kari if we overeat.

It was only until recently that I discovered how wrong my friend was in taking the verse out of the context of the verses before and after it. The entire text reads: *"When you sit to dine with a ruler, note well what is before you, and put a knife to your throat if you are given to gluttony. Do not crave his delicacies, for that food is deceptive"* (Proverbs 23:1–3). In other words, gluttony puts us at risk for being easily led astray. If you are a glutton, and you can be tempted with food, you are more likely to compromise in other areas of your life. Verse two is not a command to hurt ourselves when we sin—it's a warning from God for our protection!

When I was in the fifth grade, a little girl won 'my heart' simply by sending a pack of candy to me through a friend. I hadn't "liked" her before, but suddenly I saw her in a new light, and I was smitten. I will spare you the sordid details, but she broke my eleven-year-old heart in the end. If I hadn't been thinking with my stomach, I would not have been hurt. This was the first time (but certainly not the last) I was led astray by being tempted through food.

The STRUGGLE vs. the struggle

You may never have thought of yourself as a glutton before. I am certain that some of you are feeling shame as you read this chapter. **Don't.** It is my hope that through reading the previous chapters you have some idea of the genesis of your inappropriate relationship with food. God knew about your struggle with this sin long before you were born and since you received Jesus. He knew about it before you read this book. You have already been forgiven.

It was very difficult for me to face the reality that I was a glutton—that I had committed the sin of habitually eating and drinking in excess of what was appropriate and necessary. My faith tells me that when faced with such a horrible realization, the only thing one can do is to go to the One I had offended, namely, God. I John 1:9 states, "*If we confess our sins, he is faithful and just and will forgive us our sins and purify us from all unrighteousness.*" If you have come to the conclusion that you are a glutton, you need to do two things. First, you need to humbly admit to God that you are a glutton. Simply admit that you have sinned in this area of your life. Secondly, ask Him to forgive you. When you do this, He has promised to forgive you and that is why no shame is necessary. The price for this sin was paid for by Christ's death on the cross like all of your other sins. *End of discussion.* In fact, I believe we insult God and His Son's sacrifice when we fail to forgive ourselves and dwell in shame and self-pity.

This is why I use the term *glutton* in relation to myself in the *past tense.* I *was* a glutton but I am a glutton no more! I am free. The second part of I John 1:9 states that God will "*purify us from all our unrighteousness.*" Forgiveness is a one-time transaction canceling a debt. Purification takes time. He has begun to purify me from my sin of gluttony. I am no longer "a glutton" but I struggle with the sin of gluttony. I am still tempted to inappropriately overeat and (shock of all shocks) I sometimes give in to temptation! But I have moved from a STRUGGLE that dominated my life and stained my character to a *struggle,* an occasional bump in the road that no longer defines who I am. What is my response when I commit the sin of gluttony? I go back to the Source, confess my sin, ask for forgiveness, and move on. I strive to keep very short accounts with God.

Within a few days of realizing my freedom from being a glutton, I was verbally assaulted by someone for being overweight. For the first time in my life, I was able to respond with a tremendous inner strength. I knew that no matter how much I weighed, no matter what anyone else said, I was a free man. I did not and would not accept the shame that someone tried to lay on me or I tried to lay on myself. How wonderful! I wasn't happy about being insulted but I was happy for the opportunity to feel the joy of my freedom. I am confident you can have this experience too.

Spirit Led Eating is the opposite of gluttony. It is submitting your will and your life and your appetites over to God. He promises to guide you and helps to protect you from yourself and others in regard to food consumption. Jesus said, *"Look at the birds of the air; they do not sow or reap or store away in barns, and yet your heavenly Father feeds them. Are you not much more valuable than they?"* (Matthew 6:26) He truly loves you and He really does care about your future.

I've shared God's rules relating to how our relationship with food affects our view of ourselves and how it affects our relationship with God. In the next chapter, I want to begin discussing how our eating affects our relationships with others.

Endnotes

[1]Shwartz, M., Chambliss, H., Brownell, K., Blair, S., Billington, C. (2003). Weight bias among health care professionals specializing in obesity. *Obesity Research* 11:1033–1039.

[2]The binge/purge cycle is also a component of the eating disorders of anorexia and bulimia, which have complex causes that require treatment outside the scope of this book. If someone is engaging in the behaviors mentioned due to one of these disorders, they should be viewed as manifestations of a medical disorder. Treatment from a competent professional should be obtained.

CHAPTER 7

Influencing Others

Spirit Led Eating: Rule Number 6

*I will be vigilant about how my
eating affects others.*

"*If your brother is distressed because of what you eat, you
are no longer acting in love. Do not by your eating destroy
your brother for whom Christ died.*"
—Romans 14:15

"*For if anyone with a weak conscience sees you who have
this knowledge eating in an idol's temple, won't he be
emboldened to eat what has been sacrificed to idols?*"
—I Corinthians 8:10

Imagine that my proposal of marriage to my wife was
an invitation to join me on a long journey—a "road
trip" from one coast of the United States to the other. I
promised my wife Laura that though I didn't know how
long the Lord would allow us to travel together or all the

adventures we would encounter along the way, I would be faithful to God and His plan for our lives. I promised I would take care of her and make the trip as easy as possible. I promised to let her help me navigate—in fact, I made it clear to her that I really didn't want to embark on the journey of the rest of my life without her. I needed her and she could count on me.

We had a wonderful honeymoon. She had the map in her right hand and my hand in her left as I drove our car down the road of life. She was content and we were running along a smooth highway . . . all cylinders humming. I was in good physical shape and seemed to have my life under control.

Shortly after we were married, I took a detour without broadcasting my intentions to Laura. My detour of overeating took us in the same *general* direction but it was not the optimal path toward our destination. In all honesty, my route sometimes took us in the absolute wrong direction.

As I veered off course, the road of life immediately became bumpier. Some parts of the road had huge potholes in it and boulders were in the middle of our lane. Laura (my navigator) tried to correct my course as soon as she saw me going astray. Instead of thanking her and changing direction, I looked at her with a cold stare and told her in so many words, "Don't touch this. You can help me in ANY other area, but don't go there. I KNOW this road. I LIKE this road. Don't you dare try to tell me it's the wrong way." I drove on, full speed ahead; seemingly oblivious to how the trip was affecting Laura. As I struggled with overeating and my dieting merry-go-round, I led us further off the right path for our marriage and our family.

Other people, people who loved us, saw I was on the wrong path. Most were too afraid to broach the subject with me. Those who did have the courage to confront me I either ignored or became angry with.

Through our many years of marriage the fog I was in would sometimes lift and I would come to my senses. I would look around and say, "What on earth am I doing here? I'm fat . . . *really* fat." During these times of clarity I would often look around for someone else to blame. Laura was the natural target. I would say directly or insinuate, "You're the navigator . . . how did you get us here?" Though feeling blamed and unheard, she would look at the map and dutifully began to guide us back to the right road. But very soon, as the fog settled back over me, I would return to the bad road that I wanted to travel.

Can you imagine what it must have been like taking this journey with me?

Philippians 2:4 states, "*Each of you should look not only to your own interests, but also to the interests of others.*" We who have struggled with overeating have not only sinned against God but we have sinned against our fellow man. In order to remain free, we must acknowledge this fact and take action to sin no more. Most of the verses that are written about how our eating adversely affects others can be broken down into two broad categories: How our overeating *hurts others* and how our overeating *leads others astray.*

Hurting Others

When I married Laura, I was in good physical shape. She enjoyed my physical appearance. By indulging my sinful appetites and gaining weight, I robbed Laura of the pleasure of my body as God intended it.

In I Corinthians 7, a series of verses discusses the need for married couples to regularly celebrate their physical relationship. In verse 4 we find a key truth: "*The wife's body does not belong to her alone but also to her husband. In the same way, the husband's body does not belong to him alone but also to his wife.*" I believe that those of us who are married have a duty to maintain our physical attractiveness, as much as it depends upon us, for the benefit of our spouse.

If you're married, ask yourself these very difficult questions: "Would I be attracted to me if I was my spouse? Would I feel as loved by my spouse if they let themselves get as overweight as I have let myself become?" If your answer to either of these questions is "No," then you need to accept the horrible truth that your relationship with food has robbed your spouse of what God has said is their right.

We also hurt other loved ones. My obsession with food set a potentially dangerous example for my children. Just as if I was addicted to alcohol or other drugs, the tools of the trade of compulsive overeating (secrecy, the dieting merry-go-round, emotional peaks and valleys) demonstrated to my children that God wasn't enough for me. By relying on food to meet my needs, I taught them to turn to their own devices instead of turning to their loving Creator when in pain or in need.

When we are overweight, we keep everyone at an emotional and physical distance. We rob our family, friends, neighbors, and strangers of the joy of knowing the wonderful person that God created us to be. I Corinthians 6:19–20 says, "*Do you not know that your body is a temple of the Holy Spirit, who is in you, whom you have received from God? You are not your own; you were bought at a price. Therefore honor God with your body.*" You have an example to set in this world, an example of a loving and gracious God who reaches out to those in need, who longs to grow close to His people.

My model for living is Jesus Christ. As a husband, I am supposed to take care of Laura's needs first. As we traveled on those dark paths, I should have been attentive to the look of worry and sometimes fear in her eyes as I sped over the potholes and boulders. I thank God that He finally helped me to see how my struggle affected other people, especially Laura. From her point of view, one of the greatest things about my living out *Spirit Led Eating* is that she can now literally put her arms completely around me again. I'm allowing her to be close to me physically and emotionally.

The good news is that *Spirit Led Eating* can undo the many hurts we have done to others. It will require taking time to contemplate how your eating has hurt others in your life. You will probably need to humbly ask people how your overeating has hurt them. You will have to ask them to forgive you. They may not trust you for a while, but as you consistently live out the rules of *Spirit Led Eating*, they will notice a difference.

My son stayed overnight at a friend's house a few weeks ago. When we picked him up, we sat down and talked with the young man's parents for a while. We found out that my son had been treated to an all-you-can-eat pizza buffet the night before. As the parents described the experience, the father made a statement in passing that blew me away. He said: "Eric says you do really good with buffets. You don't lose control."

It may seem like a small thing to many of you, but inside I was screaming in response, "MY son said THAT about ME?!"

Before *Spirit Led Eating*, I was the king of buffets. Buffets were a place where I could overeat and justify it because A) I had to get my money's worth since my wife and children didn't eat enough (see chapter 4 about the lies we tell ourselves) and B) the restaurant had challenged me with the phrase 'All you can eat.' They had issued a challenge; they were *begging* me to gorge myself!

I am very blessed that even my son has begun to acknowledge my freedom. Those words replay over and over in my mind: "*Eric says you do really good with buffets.*" Neither my friend nor my son can imagine the power and glory contained in those eight little words. God keeps delivering victory upon victory to me and others who live out *Spirit Led Eating.*

Leading others astray

In I Corinthians 8, Paul describes a problem in the early church that is closely related to the problem we face when we overeat. In the city of Corinth and in other cities in the Roman world, animals were sacrificed in the names of many false gods. Christians sometimes ate the meat from these sacrifices. Like today, many of the Corinthian Christians came directly out of the culture they were born into—they had worshiped the idols that this food was being sacrificed to. To these new believers, the idea of eating food sacrificed to idols was abhorrent—it was either a painful reminder of their sinful lifestyle, or they felt there was some power attached to the meat of these sacrifices to their former gods.

Paul states in verse 4, "*We know that an idol is nothing at all in the world and that there is no God but one.*" Because there is no god but the one true God, the reality was that the food sacrificed to idols was nothing more than food—there was no supernatural quality to it. However, Paul acknowledged that at least a few believers attached *special meaning* to these foods: "*Some people are still so accustomed to idols that when they eat such food they think of it as having been sacrificed to an idol, and since their conscience is weak, it is defiled*" (vs. 7).

Paul then begins to describe the responsibility of those believers in Corinth who felt (rightly so) the liberty to eat any food provided to them by God: *"Be careful, however, that the exercise of your freedom does not become a stumbling block to the weak. For if anyone with a weak conscience sees you who have this knowledge eating in an idol's temple, won't he be emboldened to eat what has been sacrificed to idols? So this weak brother, for whom Christ died, is destroyed by your knowledge"* (vs. 9–11).

Lastly, Paul states the consequences of our failure to live up to our responsibility and what our response should be: *"When you sin against your brothers in this way and wound their weak conscience, you sin against Christ. Therefore, if what I eat causes my brother to fall into sin, I will never eat meat again, so that I will not cause him to fall"* (vs. 12–13). We influence others by what we eat.

Let's bridge the millennia between the problem that existed in Corinth and the problem of gluttony and overeating that exists today. The next time your church has a fellowship meal or picnic, I challenge you to sit at a table with overweight people—especially if there is an assortment of desserts or a dessert table present. Pay attention to the behavior of the overweight people at the table. Something like the following scenario will take place: If there are four overweight people at the table, at least one of them will *not* be on the "dieting" part of the merry-go-round—they will be eating anything they want. At least one other person will be dieting, although they may say nothing about it. The other two will be somewhere in the middle and at the very least will be self-conscious of what other people *may be* thinking about what they are eating. They won't be thinking about how their eating will affect others; they will only be wondering how others will judge them based on what they eat.

The dieter will not get dessert and thus may arrive at the table first. The self-conscious people will also arrive with no dessert but later than the dieter because they took time to look over the dessert table without getting anything. The 'anything-they-want person' will arrive with a full plate of food, put it down at the table, and immediately head to the dessert table before all the "good stuff" is taken. He will come back with a piece of cake, a piece of pie, a couple of doughnuts, and several cookies.

Someone may make a smart comment to the 'anything-goes' guy or nothing at all will be said. But watch the other three. They will take note of 'anything-goes' dessert plate and revisit it with their eyes several times throughout the meal.

As the meal is winding down, and before the dessert table is empty, one of the self-conscious people will say something like "Boy, that chocolate cake looks like Trudy made it. I haven't had a piece of Trudy's cake in a long time." As she gets up and starts toward the dessert table, the second 'self-conscious' person will say "Get me a piece of Trudy's cake while you're up please . . . but only a small piece." They will rationalize their overeating because the quantity they are eating is less than the quantity consumed by 'anything-goes.'

Look at the dieter's face at this point. You will see a look of torture because, without your knowledge or the knowledge of anyone else at the table, she has promised herself she wouldn't eat any dessert that day. However, emboldened by "Anything-goes' and influenced by the 'self-conscious' twins, the dieter will get up, go to the table, and get a couple of cookies. She never intended to violate her diet, her promise to herself, but she can now justify her overeating because it is less than the other three at the table.

The interesting thing about this scenario is that if you came back to the same table with the same people the following month, the same play would be staged, but the actors would have changed roles. 'Anything-goes' would be played by one of the self-conscious people, the other self-conscious person would become the dieter, and the dieter would have relaxed into the part of the other self-conscious person. It's an unconscious dance that all overweight people engage in with each other.

Let's complete the link between the early church scenario and the scenario of today. Is eating dessert at a church fellowship meal inherently wrong? Absolutely not; just as eating food sacrificed to idols wasn't wrong 1,950 years ago. As I said in Chapter 3, if you can truly be thankful for something, you can eat it.

However, we are called to be aware of how our behavior negatively affects those around us. One of the many reasons we should engage in *Spirit Led Eating* is so we don't cause others, especially our brothers and sisters in Christ, to stumble and fall into the sin of gluttony or of simply eating something they can't be thankful for. That is why I know that God would never allow me the freedom to gorge myself on desserts—I would certainly lead others to stumble and fall.

A few months ago, we celebrated the birthday of a co-worker with a card, a song, and (you guessed it) a cake. I was aware that at least a couple of my co-workers knew I was trying to eat differently. One person in particular seemed to struggle with the idea that *Spirit Led Eating* was not a diet. I didn't want to offend the 'birthday girl' but I didn't want to cause my friend to stumble either. So I prayed, "God, what should I do?" The Holy Spirit is so wonderful and gentle and wise. I sensed in my heart, *"Eat a small piece.*

Demonstrate that you are free today." So I ate a small piece of the cake.

The other day, now months later, the friend who didn't understand *Spirit Led Eating*, approached me and said, "I'm starting to get it. What I'm reading and studying, coupled with how you look and the freedom you walk in is starting to get to me—it takes me a while, but I eventually catch on." My freedom to eat in moderation and under the control of the Holy Spirit is influencing my friend to reconsider his concept of dieting and eating.

What you eat influences others. You have the power to hurt others by your choices and you, like me, have abused that power in the past. More importantly, however, you now have the honor of being a shining example of God's redemption and restoration by letting Him lead and guide you on a daily basis.

But God doesn't want us to stop here. The next rule takes our responsibility to others to the next level.

CHAPTER 8

Sharing

Spirit Led Eating: Rule Number 7

I will share food with others

*"John answered, "The man with two tunics should share
with him who has none, and the one who has food should
do the same."*

—Luke 3:11

*"A generous man will himself be blessed, for he shares his
food with the poor."*

—Proverbs 22:9

*"If your enemy is hungry, give him food to eat; if he is thirsty,
give him water to drink."*

—Proverbs 25:21

Throughout the scriptures, God uses food as a
metaphor by relating it to something much more
profound than it appears on the surface. I have used

many such examples in previous chapters, yet I believe that there is one food metaphor that out-shines them all. One word-picture that represents the greatest story of all time. It is re-enacted in every Christian church on a regular basis through the sacrament of Communion.

The night before Jesus died on the cross, He celebrated the Passover meal with His disciples:

"While they were eating, Jesus took bread, gave thanks and broke it, and gave it to his disciples, saying, 'Take and eat; this is my body.'

Then he took the cup, gave thanks and offered it to them, saying, 'Drink from it, all of you. This is my blood of the covenant, which is poured out for many for the forgiveness of sins."

(Matthew 26:26–28)

Jesus shared bread and wine with the disciples at the Last Supper. He shared His body and His blood with all of us when He died on the cross. He voluntarily surrendered His life so that others would benefit. *"Greater love has no one than this, that he lay down his life for his friends"* (John 15:13).

Those of us who struggle with an inappropriate relationship with food place far too much value on what we eat and drink. In a very real sense, food becomes our "life." This rule demands that we lay aside our food for the benefit of others, just as Christ laid down His life for the world. Living out this rule is integral to successfully engaging in *Spirit Led Eating.*

In God's Word, there are three groups of people that we need to focus on when it comes to feeding others: the people we see everyday, the poor and those in need, and our enemies.

Our Family, Friends & Neighbors

You would think that sharing food with family, friends and neighbors would be much easier than sharing food with those in need and with our enemies. However, sharing food with people we like can be daunting. Our selfishness often hinders our ability to live out this part of Rule Number 7. In Luke 3:11, John the Baptist states, *"The man with two tunics should share with him who has none, and the one who has food should do the same."* We are responsible for sharing with others out of our abundance.

We overeaters are hoarders. I know people who have stashes of food that they hide from others for whenever they "feel like a snack." We don't like to share because we wrongly assume we have a special right to food. We may sometimes give money to a soup kitchen or donate a few cans of green beans during a food drive, but our choicest food belongs to us.

Look in the refrigerator at your workplace. You will see bags and boxes of food with your coworkers' names labeled on each item. Ironically, much of this food will be abandoned, kept beyond the expiration date, and have to be thrown out. At one place I worked, I walked into the kitchen one afternoon to find a member of the cleaning staff filling a thirty-gallon trash can with the food we had all left in the refrigerator for weeks. As I approached her, she looked up at me, slowly shook her head, and said, "What a waste." What a waste indeed.

When I was on the dieting phase of the "merry-go-round," I would often have special foods reserved only for me. For example, if I was on a low-carb diet I would get special low-carb breads. Heaven forbid if anyone, including my children, tried to eat any of it! It was mine! I was very possessive about the foods I saw as my own.

I'm a cottage cheese fiend. Maybe it's because of my environment (I lived many years in America's Dairyland, Wisconsin). Maybe it's genetic (my father loved it and so does my son) but I truly enjoy 'curds and whey.' Throughout my children's lives, they knew they could eat anything out of the refrigerator without permission except MY cottage cheese. If they did eat it I would become *hurt and angry*. These are interesting emotions to attach to a food item. It illustrates that I valued the food more than the feelings and needs of those closest to me.

No wonder God tells us to share: *"For where your treasure is, there your heart will be also"* (Luke 12:34). We who struggle with an inappropriate relationship with food need to be reminded to share with others, even those closest to us. We must constantly ask ourselves if we treasure food more than people.

Make a list of all the foods that are your favorites. Do you have a secret stash of them in your home, your office, or your garage? Expose them to the light of day and give it all away. Take a friend to lunch and pick up the tab. Put a bag of apples in the refrigerator at work with a sticky-note that says, "Take one!" It is freeing and feels very good when you share.

Remember, you don't have to hoard food; God provides the food you need on a daily basis. Hoarding food only creates distance between you and those you love.

My children now know they can help themselves to anything in the house with impunity—but it took them a while. They checked with me for months before eating certain foods, especially the "sacred" cottage cheese. One of the biggest changes they tell me they notice in me since I began living out *Spirit Led Eating* is my openness in sharing food. I still struggle with the pull to be possessive at times, but like every other area of *Spirit Led Eating*, God brings greater victory every day.

The Poor and Needy

In Western culture, food is everywhere: convenience stores, super-markets, and restaurants are on almost every street corner. New reports seem to be released daily discussing the problem of obesity in our nation. We forget about the hungry people in our communities and the people who are starving to death worldwide every day.

I live in one of the most affluent counties in our state. When I drop my daughter off at the local high school, I see sixteen-year-olds driving brand new luxury cars and SUV's. I don't see or think about the poverty around me as often as I should.

We often have cultural and spiritual biases against the poor. I was raised to believe that people should "pull themselves up by their bootstraps" and take care of themselves and their families. I have always prided myself on my independence and self-reliance and took it as a sign of weakness when I had to ask for help. In relation to providing food to those in need, I have often heard 2 Thessalonians 3:10 quoted: *"If a man will not work, he shall not eat."* This is a wise way of dealing with someone who refuses to take care of himself. But there are many more verses and examples of giving food away in the Bible than there are verses about withholding food in a disciplinary manner.

I recently had lunch with the director of a local ministry that provides food to the poor. She told me that her ministry needs 1000 pounds of food every week to meet the demand in our community. A half-ton is a lot of food, considering there are other ministries and organizations in the area that provide food to the poor and homeless. If the need is that great in my little part of the world, think of the need on a global scale! Thinking like that will make you look at a chocolate sundae with new eyes.

There are several reasons I believe God tells us to give food to those in need. Proverbs 22:9 states, "*A generous man will himself be blessed, for he shares his food with the poor.*" We are blessed by God and feel good about ourselves when we give unselfishly.

More importantly, when we begin to think about and help meet the concrete needs of others, we will be less inclined to take what we have for granted. When we are focusing on the needs of others, we are much less likely to act out selfishly. By giving our food to those in need, we don't have as much time, energy, and resources to sinfully indulge our own appetites.

Our motivation should primarily be the well-being of others. In Matthew 15, we read about Jesus miraculously feeding four thousand people using just seven loaves of bread and a few small fish (vs. 34). His reason for doing so was not so they would stay and listen to Him or because He wanted to show them how powerful He was. They had been hanging on His every word and watching Him perform miracles for days. Jesus was motivated by His love for them: "*I have compassion for these people; they have already been with me three days and have nothing to eat. I do not want to send them away hungry, or they may collapse on the way*" (vs. 32).

I am biased but I believe I attend one of the best churches in the world. Led by Pastor Ken Jumper, the Harvest in Lexington, SC has the mission of "Creating a Place of Love and Grace for All People." Because of our mission, we have many ministries related to the care of people in need. One such ministry, *Recovery Place*, is a constellation of support groups for people experiencing grief, recovery from addictions, couples contemplating divorce, and men, women, and children reeling from the effects of separation and divorce.

When director Cindi Stone started this ministry, the focus was on this latter group (divorce recovery) and she knew there would be an inherent problem serving this population. This ministry would need to be held in the evening so participants could work and/or go to school during the day. After a long day, single parents didn't have the time and energy to go home, prepare a meal, and then attend the meeting. They also couldn't afford to pay for their family to eat out every week. So for 13 Mondays in the fall and 13 Mondays in the spring, a free dinner is given to everyone who walks in the doors of The Harvest. The food is donated and served by volunteers. Participants in every support group now benefit from this tradition. It grew out of Cindi's compassion for those in need and her wisdom in knowing that sometimes you need to feed peoples' stomachs before you can feed their souls.

There are many ways you and I can live out this part of *Spirit Led Eating*. We can choose not to eat for an entire day and contribute the money to a local food pantry. We can take part of our food budget and participate in a canned food drive. We can bring a meal to a single mother and her children that live in our apartment complex or neighborhood. We can forego going out for brunch one Sunday and send an anonymous monetary gift to someone in dire financial straights folded in a piece of paper with the words "With Love from Jesus" printed on it.

Our Enemies

When I was in first grade, I liked a little girl named Heather. My friends and I would sometimes chase her and her friends around the playground. This would now be called sexual harassment. When I would occasionally catch her (for she was a fast little girl), I would ask her if she liked me. She would always say, "I don't like you . . . I like James." James was my enemy. He was better looking and more popular than I was and we both knew it. As we got older, I realized that James was a pretty nice guy and couldn't help how wonderful he was. But for that year, because he had something I wanted and couldn't have (namely Heather's affections), he was my enemy.

I had an enemy in high school for a while. I never found out why the guy didn't like me. He opposed me whenever he could, made light of any misfortune that befell me, and tried to make me look bad in front of our peers. He was my enemy.

I have had enemies as an adult. I have had people interfere with good work I was trying to accomplish simply because it wasn't their idea. I've had people threaten to hurt me physically because they didn't agree with a decision I've made. They were my enemies.

You may have an enemy of your own. He may be a neighbor whose dog always uses your lawn as its personal restroom. She may be that parent on the PTA who is trying to start a program that you know is a waste of time and money. Perhaps even a sibling is angry with you for some real or imagined wrong you committed several years ago and has cut you out of his life.

So it's very interesting to me that God says through the writer of Proverbs, "*If your enemy is hungry, give him food to eat; if he is thirsty, give him water to drink*" (vs. 25:21). When someone doesn't like me, when they purpose themselves against me for whatever reason, one of the last things that I want to do is to share my food and drink with them. In

98

fact, withholding these types of essentials is an excellent way of communicating without using words, "I know what you're up to. I know you're not my friend. And I'm going to show you just what I think of you." However, as Christians we are to live out Romans 12:18 which states, *"If it is possible, as far as it depends on you, live at peace with everyone."* This is often very hard to do when others don't want to be at peace with us. Thankfully, God gave us a great example of a man who shared food with his enemies in the first book of the Bible.

Beginning in chapter 37 of Genesis, we read the story of Joseph. Joseph was a dreamer and an interpreter of dreams. Though blessed by God, he was proud and spoiled by his father. His brothers didn't like the way they were treated in comparison to Joseph, so some of them plotted to kill him. One of his brothers was kind enough to intervene, so Joseph wasn't murdered. Instead, he was assaulted, sold into slavery, and his father was told he was mauled by an animal and died. He was out of his brothers' (his "enemies") lives forever . . . or so they thought.

As a slave, Joseph did well and garnered the favor of his master. Because he was attractive, he also earned the unwanted affections of his master's wife. When he rejected her, she falsely accused him of trying to sleep with her and he was sent to prison. Several years later, because of his God-given ability to interpret dreams, he was released from prison, and was made the number two man in the kingdom of Egypt. For seven years he organized the resources of the nation to help them prepare for the global famine that was revealed in the dream he interpreted. Egypt prospered while the rest of the world began to starve.

Joseph's family, devastated by the famine, heard there was food in Egypt. So his brothers, his mortal enemies, came to beg for food, not knowing that Joseph was the man they would have to ask. Joseph did not reveal his identity to them immediately in order to determine that they had changed and their motives were pure, but eventually he told them the truth about who he was.

Joseph could have sent them away to starve to death. He could have enslaved or killed them. But instead he shared his food with them and he explained why in Genesis 45: "*And now, do not be distressed and do not be angry with yourselves for selling me here, because it was to save lives that God sent me ahead of you. For two years now there has been famine in the land, and for the next five years there will not be plowing and reaping. But God sent me ahead of you to preserve for you a remnant on earth and to save your lives by a great deliverance. So then, it was not you who sent me here, but God*" (vs. 5–8). Through all of his trials, Joseph learned that God could use even his enemies to bring blessing to him in the long run.

God says in Proverbs 25:22 that by giving food and drink to our enemy we will "*heap burning coals on his head . . .*" When we are kind to those who oppose us, it makes no sense to them and may even be painful for them to endure because they know they don't deserve kind treatment. Just as it can send a powerfully negative message when we withhold food from an enemy, it can send an equally powerful positive one when we provide it. The act of sharing may be the first step in ending the enmity between you and your enemy. What a wonderful picture of God's love for us!

Verse 22 concludes with the phrase, "*. . . and the LORD will reward you.*" The Lord will reward us for two reasons. First, God rewards obedience. Remember that *Spirit Led Eating* centers not on obedience to our own wants, needs, or appetites, but on obedience to God and His Word. Secondly, by showing kindness to an enemy we get out of the way so God is allowed to work: "*Do not take revenge, my* *friends, but leave room for God's wrath, for it is written: "It is mine to avenge; I will repay,' says the Lord"* (Romans 12:19).

We can share food with our enemies on a practical level in many ways. For example, leave the last donut for that obnoxious co-worker who always knocks down your ideas at staff meetings. Bring food over to the sick neighbor who yelled at your kids for no reason last week. Buy coffee for the man who cut you off in traffic so he could get into the gas station before you. Because we are Christians, sharing food with our enemies may even take the form of supporting a ministry that provides food to the children of a nation that is at war with yours.

We've discussed how our eating affects our relationship with God and how it affects our relationship with others. In the next chapter we will learn about the rule that completes *Spirit Led Eating*. Rule number eight dispels the myth that we must suffer in order to be obedient.

CHAPTER 9

Enjoy!

Spirit Led Eating: Rule Number 8

I will enjoy the food that I am thankful for.

"He provides food for those who fear him; he remembers his covenant forever."
—*Psalm 111:5*

"Go, eat your food with gladness . . . for it is now that God favors what you do."
—*Ecclesiastes 9:7*

Imagine you are about to sit down with your family for a traditional Thanksgiving dinner. In your mind's eye, picture all of the sumptuous foods before you. There's roast turkey, dressing, sweet *and* mashed potatoes, fresh corn, cranberries, green bean casserole, and steaming-hot biscuits. Pumpkin and apple pies are cooling on the counter in the kitchen. (Is your mouth watering yet?) You can almost feel the warmth of your family and friends. You are truly thankful to God for all He has done for you. But your attention is drawn back to the food, the feast set before you. What are you allowed to eat? What food should you avoid? What are you going to do about *all of this food*?

Changing Your Mind

Just as we have had to change the way we think about how we view food in relationship with God and others, we need to learn how to react to the food God provides.

We read in Psalm 111:5, "*He provides food for those who fear him; He remembers his covenant forever.*"

God has provided me with a lot. He's given me an amazing wife, wonderful children, fulfilling work, great friends, a fun car to drive, a nice house . . . I could go on and on. How does God want me to react to these things? He wants me to *enjoy* them. He wants us to be thankful for everything and, as an outgrowth of our gratitude, He desires that we experience pleasure from the people and things He provides. "*A man can do nothing better than to eat and drink and find satisfaction in his work. This too, I see, is from the hand of God, for without him, who can eat or find enjoyment?*" (Ecclesiastes 2:24–25).

Therefore, if we can be thankful for the food God gives us, we are free to enjoy it. We can savor the tastes and textures of the food we eat. We have the freedom to slow down. When I began to live out *Spirit Led Eating*, my reaction to the experience of eating changed. I tasted some of my favorite foods like I never had before. We can now delight in new culinary experiences. Without the guilt and shame of our past inappropriate relationship with food, we are free to enjoy the experience of eating.

Daunting choices

Prior to *Spirit Led Eating*, we had only two choices when it came to meals like the one I described at the beginning of this chapter. If we are dieting, we can choose to take very *small* portions of *some* of the foods before us or we can choose to eat something completely different than the traditional meal. We then feel left out—alienated from the family and friends we're supposed to be celebrating with. Because of our feelings of isolation, later we may steal some of the "forbidden" foods in order to feel better. We leave the holiday feeling worse than when we entered it.

The other choice involves our uncanny ability to rationalize our behavior in order to binge. We may say to ourselves, "It's Thanksgiving! I'm supposed to overeat. I *deserve* to overeat." We load our plates and gorge ourselves. We use a date on the calendar to justify our gluttony. Food then becomes the event. We may extend our binge for several days until the last piece of turkey is devoured and the last slice of pumpkin pie is gone. This eventually leads to feelings of disappointment, guilt and shame. We leave the holiday season much heavier then when we entered it. We get back on the dieting merry-go-round.

Spirit Led Eating gives us a third option to this scenario. It involves retooling our brains to look at special occasions like Thanksgiving, Christmas, and even our birthdays from a very different point of view.

Food and Feelings

As I was doing the research in God's Word that led to the revelation of *Spirit Led Eating*, I was often surprised. Of all the rules—this one surprised me the most. I said in chapter one that part of the process of discovering

Spirit Led Eating involved writing down principles I had learned from diet and nutrition books I'd read in the past. I added that some of these principles needed to be amended or abandoned.

One such principle, based on an assumption I had been working under for years, was that we should not use food to alter our mood. I believed food should be avoided when it came to changing the way we feel. I based this assumption on two things that I had come to believe about food and our relationship to it.

First, we know that food has a tremendous impact on our minds and our emotions. There are several excellent books that document these connections.[1] We often medicate our feelings by overeating instead of turning to God or others who can help us. Experts in the field of food addiction state that we should identify those foods we rely on to medicate our feelings (such as starches, sugars, or fats) and abstain from them completely. The Bible even seems to support this in verses that state we should avoid anything that may cause us to sin: *"And if your eye causes you to sin, pluck it out. It is better for you to enter the kingdom of God with one eye than to have two eyes and be thrown into hell"* (Mark 9:47).

Secondly, I had learned that food should only be thought of as fuel—like gasoline in an automobile engine. This led me to believe that we should not eat food that is enjoyable to us on a regular basis. We should only eat food that is good for us. So when I was on the dieting part of the merry-go-round, I ate few things that were palatable for me. I only ate what I thought was nutritious or within my "plan." And like many of you, this left me feeling like I was missing out, like I was being deprived.

Armed with my assumptions, I searched the Bible, confident that I would find evidence supporting the belief that

God does not want us to use food to alter our emotions. However, as I read the book of Nehemiah one day, I discovered that my assumptions were completely false.

Hitting the wall

The Old Testament book of Nehemiah provides some of the best teaching on planning, leadership and overcoming adversity I have ever read. When the Babylonians conquered the city of Jerusalem in 586 b.c., they completely destroyed Jerusalem's ability to defend itself and exiled its inhabitants. As time passed, God led His people to return to the city. The rebuilding of the Temple is documented in the book of Ezra, and the rebuilding of the city walls is documented in the book of Nehemiah.

As I read the book of Nehemiah, I am struck with the symbolic parallels between the ruined walls of Jerusalem and the ruined lives of the people of Israel. The walls were broken and the people were broken. Enemies from without and within did not want them to rebuild their lives and their city. Enter Nehemiah.

Nehemiah had earned great favor with the King of Babylon and had his financial and moral support in rebuilding the wall. Most of the book of Nehemiah documents the struggles faced by this courageous leader as he accomplished God's will for his life and his people. As the people of Israel were rebuilding the wall, they were also rebuilding their lives, their community, and their sense of identity as the people of God.

When the wall was completed, the entire community gathered together in the square in front of one of the city gates.

"So on the first day of the seventh month Ezra the priest brought the Law before the assembly, which was made up

*of men and women and all who were able to understand.
He read it aloud from daybreak till noon as he faced the
square before the Water Gate in the presence of the men,
women and others who could understand. And all the people
listened attentively to the Book of the Law"*
(Nehemiah 8:2–3).

As they heard Ezra read the Word of God, they re-
acted strongly. They realized that their behavior had not
been acceptable to God. In verse 9 we read that the people
were deeply moved: *"all the people had been weeping as
they listened to the words of the Law."* They were sad when
they heard God's Word because they knew that they had
drifted far from His ideal. In my previous thinking about
food, I would have assumed that this moment would have
been a great time to fast and pray—to accept punish-
ment, to atone for individual and community sins, and a
time to abstain from food out of respect and fear of ap-
pearing unrepentant.

The next verse, however, forever shattered my assumptions about food and mood.

*"Nehemiah said, "Go and enjoy choice food and sweet
drinks, and send some to those who have nothing prepared.
This day is sacred to our Lord. Do not grieve, for the joy of
the LORD is your strength."*
(vs. 8:10)

**God, through his leader Nehemiah, told the people of
God to comfort themselves with food!** When I saw this
truth for the first time, I was dumbfounded. I thought, "This
can't be right. We're not supposed to eat food when we're
sad in order to feel better. I did that my entire life with
disastrous results!"

So I began searching his Word to find other instances of God leading people to food in order to feel better. I've already mentioned the depressed and exhausted Elijah in I Kings 19 being directed by an angel to "*Get up and eat*" (vs. 5). When Paul (then known as Saul) was healed from his blindness after the encounter with Christ on the road to Damascus he was baptized and "*after taking some food, he regained his strength*" (Acts 9:19). Hannah, "*in bitterness of soul*" *cried out to the Lord to give her a son.* After being blessed by God's priest she "*went her way and ate, and her face was no longer sad*" (I Samuel 1:18).

Therefore, I have come to believe that there are times that God, through His Holy Spirit, may lead us to eat certain foods in order to find comfort in times of sorrow. During these times we are supposed to accept God's provision with gratitude and enjoy what He provides.

These special times should be rare and are very different from the overeating we used to indulge in when we ate to feel better. Then we ate at almost any provocation—an argument with a spouse, a stressful day at work, or after having received an unexpected bill. As you can see from the examples above, what I am describing is *Spirit Led Eating* in response to difficult emotions that is time-limited. It should also be in response to specific events like the death of a loved one or after having fought an exhausting spiritual battle. We should enjoy the food God provides for us when we are sad only if He is the one who directed us to partake—not when we are self-directed.

Several years ago I was hospitalized for acute pancreatitis—my pancreas simply stopped working and my entire digestive system was temporarily shut down. The pain was excruciating. The doctors prescribed a very potent drug to deaden the pain. It did so effectively. As my pancreas began to function again, the pain subsided along with my need for the medication. Had I made the decision to lie about my pain in order to continue receiving the medication, I would have been *abusing* the drug the doctor had prescribed for me. I could be (and was) thankful for the medicine when it was first administered, but I could not have been thankful had I made the choice to abuse it. Similarly, if God, through the Holy Spirit, leads us to *temporarily* eat more than usual during times of bereavement or spiritual exhaustion, and we choose to overeat when the prescribed time is past, then we are *abusing* His grace and provision. We cannot eat with thanksgiving.

Times of Feasting

Throughout the Old Testament, we see God proclaiming days of sacrifice and feasting. In Leviticus 23, the feasts of Passover, First-fruits, the Feast of Weeks, the Feast of Trumpets, the Day of Atonement, and other feasts are described. These were (and still are) times of corporate worship, solemnity, sacrifice and eating.

In the book of Esther we read that genocide is averted by God's intervention through Mordecai, a man of courage and strength of character, and through his niece Queen Esther. The community's response was the Feast of Purim, which is celebrated to this day:

> *"Mordecai recorded these events, and he sent letters to all the Jews throughout the provinces of King Xerxes, near and far, to have them celebrate annually the fourteenth and fifteenth days of the month of Adar as the time when the Jews got relief from their enemies, and as the month when their sorrow was turned into joy and their mourning into a day of celebration. He wrote them to observe the days as days of feasting and joy and giving presents of food to one another and gifts to the poor."*
> (Esther 9:20–22)

The Old and New Testaments describe several examples of joy-inspired eating. We may feast out of a sense of hospitality. In 2 Kings 6:23, we read that the prophet Elisha ordered a "great feast" for an enemy army who found themselves in the middle of Israel's capital. We read in Genesis 18:5–8, 19:3, and 24:33 that it was customary to provide special meals for travelers.

Family celebrations can be times of feasting. When the prodigal son comes to his senses and returns home from his misadventures in Luke 15, his loving father, in metaphorical representation of God's joy when we return to Him, orders "Bring the fattened calf and kill it. Let's have a feast and celebrate" (vs. 23). Abraham, to honor his son Isaac's weaning, holds a "great feast" in Genesis 21:8.

Like present-day weddings, the Bible has several examples of marital unions being commemorated by feasting. We read of Samson holding a feast in honor of his marriage in Judges 14:10. Jacob's unscrupulous father-in-law holds a wedding feast for him in Genesis 21:8. The first miracle Jesus performed was turning water into wine at a wedding banquet (John 2:1–11).

We read that even *birthdays* are an occasion to feast. Genesis 40:20 records that Pharaoh held a birthday feast. Job's sons held banquets to celebrate their birthdays (Job 1:4).

In American culture we celebrate such food-centered holidays as Christmas, Easter, the 4th of July, and last but not least, Thanksgiving. These celebrations may cause us to fall into the twin traps I described at the beginning of this chapter: withdrawing from celebrations or being gluttonous. Or they can be special times where we feel the blessing of God as we enjoy His provision.

In *Spirit Led Eating* you will find times, especially during celebrations, where the Lord allows you to eat more than usual. On the day before Thanksgiving you may be led to eat what you normally eat. The day *of* Thanksgiving, you may feel freedom to eat more than you ate the day before. Based on Biblical examples of feasting, we don't have to be surprised or fearful about eating in response to our joy.

One man who lives by the rules of *Spirit Led Eating* described a period of days before and after his birthday where he felt free to eat more than he had been accustomed to. He described feeling a little heavier than he had prior to this time of celebratory eating. But when the time of feasting was over, at the beginning of the new week, he was led by the Holy Spirit to return to his usual eating habits. A few days later, the "heavy" feeling was gone.

Turning to food instead of God to fill our empty spaces and relieve our pain is wrong. We must be on our guard and accept the truth that we may be tempted to use our freedom as an excuse to overeat (Romans 6:1).

With these truths in mind, I pray that this final rule changes your thinking and feelings regarding the experience of eating as it has mine. We are free to savor and enjoy the food that God provides for us. We no longer need to feel pressure at the onset of the holiday season. We no longer need to experience the fear of being alienated from our family and friends. We no longer have to worry about becoming out of control. We can be free from these negative emotions.

Now that you are armed with a thorough understanding of each of the eight rules of *Spirit Led Eating*, you are ready to begin to walk in them. The next and final chapter will help you prepare to be free, if you are ready, for the rest of your life.

Endnote

[1]See Kay Sheppard's *From the First Bite* (Health Communications, 2000) and Gary Smalley's, *Food and Love* (Tyndale House, 2001).

CHAPTER 10

Walking In Freedom

"I will walk about in freedom, for I have sought out your precepts."

—**Psalm 119:45**

There's an old joke that travels in professional counseling circles and it goes like this: *"How many counselors does it take to change a light bulb?"* The answer: *"One. But the light bulb has to want to be changed."* The same is true about you and your relationship to food.

Even Jesus acknowledged that just because someone *looks* as if he or she is ready to change, it doesn't mean he *is* ready to change. In John chapter 5 we read about a disabled man near the pool of Bethesda. For 38 years, he had struggled with his condition. Part of this time was spent waiting near this pool in hopes that he would be able to enter the waters at the right time and receive healing. Considering the length of time he had lived with his disability and the extreme and frustrating measures he was willing to endure in order to find a cure, I find Jesus' first question to him rather interesting:

"Do you want to get well?"

(vs. 6)

The man's reply, as recorded in vs. 7, contained the excuse that he could never enter the pool at the right time because others would crowd him out before he reached it. Jesus responds by healing him: *"Get up! Pick up your mat and walk"* (vs. 8). We can't know for sure why Jesus asked him that question, but I believe we can glean truth from such a seemingly obvious query.

I was that man. I hadn't been physically disabled for 38 years, but I had been emotionally disabled and in bondage to my relationship with food for 24 years. I had created my own "mat" of fat. I too had struggled to enter my own "pools of Bethesda" in the form of the many diets and exercise programs I had tried. I too struggled with hopelessness and self-pity. And when I approached the Lord and asked Him to heal me He would ask me, *"Do you want to get well?"*

Continuing the metaphor of the man at the pool of Bethesda, when God asked me this question it was as if I rose up on my elbows from my mat, raised an eyebrow toward the Son of God and said, "DUH! Why do you think I've been lying here all this time? Why do you think I have been struggling to enter the pool at the right moment? Why do you think I've tried all these different diet regimens and suffered so much? Why do you think I've joined so many health clubs? Of course I want to be healed. Do something Jesus!"

Jesus died for you and me. He died for our sins of gluttony, pride, and putting the idol of food before our relationship with Him. He has been ready to heal you since the day you first gave in to temptation.

The healing He is ready to provide in this area is unlike any healing you have received before. The benefits of your previous diets lasted only as long as you stayed on the diet. We must maintain a certain level of physical activity for exercise to continue controlling our weight. All of our myriad attempts to control food and weight will work for a time (maybe six months to a year) but they are all temporary.

God's healing is eternal. The story of the man at the pool of Bethesda concludes with the statement, *"At once the man was cured; he picked up his mat and walked"* (vs. 9). We would all agree that it is highly unlikely that six months to a year after meeting Jesus, the man suddenly became disabled again. His healing was immediate and it was permanent.

When I began to walk in the rules of *Spirit Led Eating*, my healing was immediate. I was free for the first time in my life. I was the light bulb that wanted to be changed. Many months have passed, but I know that as long as I walk in the truths summarized by the eight rules for *Spirit Led Eating*, I will remain free. I am not in bondage to the rules as I was in bondage to a diet plan. I am free.

It all starts with the question of the light bulb. Do you want to be changed? Or will you choose to continue monitoring and controlling your weight? Will you continue to insist on the method by which you will be healed? Today I think the Lord is asking you His very simple yet profound question once again:

"Do you want to get well?"

Take a moment to think about that question. When you are ready, write your answer to the right of it. A simple "Yes, Lord" or "No, Lord" will suffice.

Starting Your Journey

An ancient Chinese proverb states, "A journey of a thousand miles begins with a single step." If you answered in the affirmative to the question above, you have taken the first step. However, any journey is made up of more than the first step. The following are my recommended next steps as you begin to live out *Spirit Led Eating*.

Fasting

Several years ago I led a men's Bible study. We discussed what God was teaching us and shared struggles and triumphs. One time I asked for prayer regarding my struggle with weight. One of my skinny friends said, "I know this may seem obvious, but have you tried fasting?" I chuckled at him condescendingly as if he didn't know what he was talking about.

My response to his question was based on the two standard reactions of those who struggle with an inappropriate relationship with food have to the subject of fasting. One reaction is that we can't imagine denying ourselves food for any reason. We *want* food. We *need* food. By suggesting we not eat, others may as well be suggesting we not breathe. The other reaction is "Yea! By not eating, I'll lose weight! Sign me up!" Both of these reactions are carnal responses to a spiritual act. This is why I looked at my friend and his suggestion with a jaundiced eye. At that time, I simply equated fasting with not eating. It is so much more than that.

Fasting is a spiritual discipline. Unlike dieting, it is not a physical discipline. God knows we need food to survive. He created us to need it! This is one of the many reasons why denying ourselves of food is such a tremendous spiritual act. In true fasting, we are denying our human needs for a season for spiritual, not physical, purposes. The scriptures are replete with examples of those who fast. Jesus fasted in the desert for 40 days and nights (Matthew 4:2). Daniel entered into a fast of certain foods for three weeks: *"I ate no choice food; no meat or wine touched my lips"* (Daniel 10:3). In the early church, our spiritual forefathers regularly fasted on an individual and corporate basis (Acts 13:2–3, 14:23).

Spirit Led Eating and fasting are not directly related and we must separate them in our minds. It may help to view fasting as Spirit Led *Not* Eating. Fasting should not be done to lose weight or viewed as something we must suffer through as a mystical way to get closer to God.

I'll use a comparison to explain one way to look at fasting. You may think it odd since I counsel and train people for a living, but I rely heavily on technology to do what I do. I use a desktop computer at home and one at work for writing, billing, and communicating through e-mail. I have a personal digital assistant (PDA) to keep track of my schedule, phone numbers, to-do list, and to take notes on. I use a laptop computer and projector to display presentations when I train people. Even though I depend on these technological devices, they sometimes fail me. They quit working like they should as if they had a mind of their own. When this happens all that is usually necessary to get them to do what they are supposed to do is to hit the RESET button.

Fasting, for me, is sometimes like hitting a spiritual RESET button. I fast when I realize something is getting in

119

the way of my relationship with God; when I "quit working" like I should. I am still tempted to put food ahead of God. I am also tempted to put other things like my relationship with my wife, my children, or work ahead of God. So when I feel that I am getting out of balance in one of these areas, I enter into a time of fasting. The first time I engaged in *Spirit Led Eating*, I did not eat any food for twenty-four hours prior to beginning. This reset my mind and body to be better able to hear God's voice instead of my own physical and emotional urges.

I also fast when I need a spiritual breakthrough. I am fasting from food but not water as I write this chapter. I care deeply about what I write and don't take the spiritual ramifications of my words lightly. I want to make sure that God and I are on the same page (pun intended). Remember that although fasting involves not eating, it has very little to do with food.

I highly recommend entering into a specific time of fasting before beginning *Spirit Led Eating*. I fasted for a day but God may lead you to fast for more or less time. If you have any health problems or special dietary requirements, please consult your physician before fasting. My wife is diabetic and cannot go without eating even one meal. If she fasts, it is only from certain foods. Talk to your Pastor or read a book on the subject of fasting. I encourage you to learn the theory and application of this spiritual discipline prior to engaging in it.[1] When I speak of fasting in this chapter I urge you not to withhold water from yourself—this is very dangerous.

Be Vigilant

My friend Shawn has a special place in my heart for a very specific reason. His example demonstrates the power of staying vigilant when you set your heart on a particular course of action. I had the privilege of attending a Bible study that he was leading one morning. The other participants happened to include some men who had known Shawn longer than he had been a Christian. Shawn shared with the group that shortly after becoming a Christian, he had written out chapter 13 of I Corinthians on the inside cover of his Bible. He read some of the words, *"Love is patient, love is kind. It does not envy, it does not boast, it is not proud. It is not rude, it is not self-seeking, it is not easily angered, it keeps no record of wrongs. Love does not delight in evil but rejoices with the truth. It always protects, always trusts, always hopes, always perseveres. Love never fails"* (vs. 4–8). Shawn continued by telling us before he was a Christian that he wouldn't let anyone hurt him. He would always get the last word in and would strike first if he felt threatened by others. His old friends agreed that Shawn had been a person not to be trifled with—they chuckled as they remembered a couple of people who tried to pull one over on Shawn only to bear the brunt of his anger. Shawn concluded his time of sharing by stating that by reading and reflecting on the truths written in the cover of his Bible on a daily basis, he hoped to someday change and learn how to love like that. I interrupted my friend and said, "Shawn, you already are a different man; you already love like that."

His friends didn't know it, but only weeks before I had betrayed Shawn. I had hurt him. When I went to him and asked his forgiveness he said, "I already forgave you. I knew that you wouldn't have done it unless you had a very good reason." Shawn was patient, kind, was not self-seeking, and was not easily angered. He kept no record of my wrong and he always trusted and hoped. By staying vigilant and keeping God's Word in the forefront of his heart and his Bible, Shawn became a new man.

When God revealed the eight rules of *Spirit Led Eating*, I became worried that I would forget the truths contained in them. I knew myself well enough to know that if I didn't keep them in the forefront of my mind, I ran the risk of forgetting.

I borrowed the underlying principle of Deuteronomy 11:18 which reads, *"Fix these words of mine in your hearts and minds; tie them as symbols on your hands and bind them on your foreheads."* I printed out business cards with the eight rules and their primary scripture references. I kept one in my billfold and my PDA case for months. I created a desktop background on my computer at work so that every time I look at my monitor, they are directly in front of me. I review them almost daily.

In Appendix A, I have included a list of all of the Rules for *Spirit Led Eating* and their scripture references. Please feel free to copy these pages and put them in the front of your Bible, on your refrigerator, in your car, or in your office. Consider writing out the scripture references on index or blank business cards and keep them in your pocket or purse. Review them regularly, especially when you feel you are struggling.

Spirit Led Eating is not a weight loss program. It is primarily about your relationship with God. It is also about spiritual, emotional, and physical freedom from an inappropriate relationship with food. One thing we should *not* be vigilant about is how much we weigh. If you worry about how much weight you have lost or not lost, your focus will be on the other side of the dieting coin.

I pray that your vigilance does not become legalistic or reminiscent of a strict dieting program. However, I Peter 5:8 reminds us, *"Be self-controlled and alert. Your enemy the devil prowls around like a roaring lion looking for someone to devour."*

Exchange

In Chapter 2 I challenged you to pray, asking God to free you. I warned you that if you prayed that prayer you would be giving up a lot. Thinking about, obtaining, hiding, cooking, and eating food takes a lot of time and energy. When God frees you from bondage, you will find you have much more of both commodities. If you don't find good things to replace the destructive thoughts and habits, you run the risk of falling back into them.

Jesus warned about this in a parable about a man who was demon possessed: *"When an evil spirit comes out of a man, it goes through arid places seeking rest and does not find it. Then it says, 'I will return to the house I left.' When it arrives, it finds the house unoccupied, swept clean and put in order. Then it goes and takes with it seven other spirits more wicked than itself, and they go in and live there. And the final condition of that man is worse than the first"* (Matthew 12:43–45).

So we need to exchange our unhealthy thoughts and habits for good ones.

You will have time to build friendships, get reacquainted with your spouse, or take a pottery class. Read a new book or better yet, write one! Perhaps you want to exercise or become more physically active. Pursue a college degree or a new ministry. By giving up your old habits of either overeating or dieting, you will free up much of your time.

I was flabbergasted by how much more I was able to accomplish in a day by not obsessing about what, where, and with whom I was going to eat my next meal. I became much more professionally and personally productive and I am confident you will too. Be careful, however, that whatever you choose to accomplish doesn't itself become an obsession.

Fellowship

"Two are better than one,
because they have a good return for their work:
If one falls down,
his friend can help him up.
But pity the man who falls
and has no one to help him up!
Also, if two lie down together, they will keep warm.
But how can one keep warm alone?
Though one may be overpowered,
two can defend themselves.
A cord of three strands is not quickly broken."

(Ecclesiastes 4: 9–12)

Most of us have fought our previous battles with food alone. Sometimes we became disillusioned because we didn't think our spouses or our friends understood what we were going through. We isolated ourselves. Like the passage above indicates, when we fight alone, it is very easy for us to fall, to be out in the cold, and to become overpowered.

My friend Robert has made my journey a joy. I believe that without our fellowship I would have been free from my old struggle, but it would have been much slower going and it would have been lonelier. As someone who is a professional when it comes to building and maintaining relationships, I wish I could say that my friendship with Robert was my idea, but it wasn't. Robert made the first move. He took a risk one day and approached me with a question about overeating. Had he not had the courage to do so, he may still be in bondage and this book would not have been written.

If you have accepted the challenge of defeating this dragon of overeating in your life, you are a courageous person. Pray about and find someone who struggles with an inappropriate relationship with food. Courageously ask them if they are ready to be free and if they want to fight along side of you. If the first person you approach tells you they are not interested, ask someone else. I am confident that you can find someone—there are millions of us who struggle.

When you find a friend or two, read this book together. Meet on a regular basis. Discuss your joys and burdens. Share what God is doing in your new life. You can use the questions in the study guide contained in appendix B to get you started. Pray together.

It is my deep and solemn hope that you will find and walk in the freedom of *Spirit Led Eating*. You are about to embark on an amazing journey where you will find the life that God always intended for you to live. You will hear His voice more clearly not just when it comes to eating, but in everything. I think it fitting to close by reminding you that God has always known of your struggle.

Jesus, in His first public proclamation about Himself took the scroll of the prophet Isaiah. And as he unrolled it, he forever reminded us of His true purpose in coming to Earth:

"The Spirit of the Lord is on me,
because he has anointed me
to preach good news to the poor.
He has sent me to proclaim freedom for the prisoners
and recovery of sight for the blind,
to release the oppressed,
to proclaim the year of the Lord's favor."
(Luke 4:18–19)

It is indeed the year of the Lord's favor in your life. Let me close with a prayer:

Lord, thank you for revealing these truths to us. I pray for the men and women who have read these words and have decided to trust you with their lives in new ways through living out the rules of Spirit Led Eating. Bless them for their new obedience to you. Bless their families as they begin to embrace and accept the changes you are bringing about in the lives of their loved ones. Finally Lord, bless the people who do not yet know You as Savior and Lord but who will be inspired to make a positive decision about You as they see Your children find true freedom and joyfully walking in obedience. May You be glorified in our obedience to Your Word. Amen.

Thank you for sharing your precious time by reading this book. I would like to know how *Spirit Led Eating* has helped you. As you begin living out these truths, please share your stories at *www.spiritledeating.com.* May God richly bless you.

Endnote

[1] Two resources that have made a tremendous impact on my understanding of fasting have been Bill Bright's book, *7 Basic Steps to Successful Fasting & Prayer* (New Life Publications, 2001) and the third chapter of Richard Foster's *Celebration of Discipline* (Harper-Collins, 1998).

Rules For Spirit Led Eating

1. I will seek God's will for my life every day—I will put food in its rightful place.

   "Jesus answered, "It is written: 'Man does not live on bread alone."
   —Luke 4:4

   "For the kingdom of God is not a matter of eating and drinking, but of righteousness, peace and joy in the Holy Spirit,"
   —Romans 14:17

2. I will thank God before eating anything and will not eat or drink anything I cannot thank God for.

   "Taking the five loaves and the two fish and looking up to heaven, he gave thanks and broke them."
   —Luke 9:16a

"But the man who has doubts is condemned if he eats, because his eating is not from faith; and everything that does not come from faith is sin."
—Romans 14:23

3. I will not lie about what or how much I eat.

"Stolen water is sweet; food eaten in secret is delicious!" But little do they know that the dead are there, that her guests are in the depths of the grave."
—Proverbs 9:17–18

"Food gained by fraud tastes sweet to a man, but he ends up with a mouth full of gravel."
—Proverbs 20:17

4. I will not complain about the food God provides for me.

". . . they spoke against God and against Moses, and said, "Why have you brought us up out of Egypt to die in the desert? There is no bread! There is no water! And we detest this miserable food!"
—Numbers 21:5

"Therefore I tell you, do not worry about your life, what you will eat or drink; or about your body, what you will wear. Is not life more important than food, and the body more important than clothes?"
—Matthew 6:25

5. I will repent every time I am guilty of gluttony or obsess about food.

"Do not join those who drink too much wine or gorge themselves on meat, for drunkards and glut-

tons become poor, and drowsiness clothes them in rags."
—Proverbs 23:21

"When you sit to dine with a ruler, note well what is before you, and put a knife to your throat if you are given to gluttony. Do not crave his delicacies, for that food is deceptive."
—Proverbs 23:1–3

6. I will be vigilant about how my eating affects others.

"If your brother is distressed because of what you eat, you are no longer acting in love. Do not by your eating destroy your brother for whom Christ died."
— Romans 14:15

"For if anyone with a weak conscience sees you who have this knowledge eating in an idol's temple, won't he be emboldened to eat what has been sacrificed to idols?"
—I Corinthians 8:10

7. I will share food with others.

"John answered, "The man with two tunics should share with him who has none, and the one who has food should do the same."
—Luke 3:11

"A generous man will himself be blessed, for he shares his food with the poor."
—Proverbs 22:9

"If your enemy is hungry, give him food to eat; if he is thirsty, give him water to drink."

—Proverbs 25:21

8. I will enjoy the food that I am thankful for.

"He provides food for those who fear him; he remembers his covenant forever."

– Psalm 111:5

"Go, eat your food with gladness, and drink your wine with a joyful heart, for it is now that God favors what you do."

—Ecclesiastes 9:7

Questions for Individual and Group Study

Chapter 1

1. The author shared that food was "my comforter, my secret friend, my source of pleasure and joy." How would you describe your past and present relationship with food?

2. List all of the attempts you have made to control your own weight including diets, exercise programs, and other ways. How long were you able to stick with each of them before going back to your old habits?

3. In what ways has food become a 'god' in your life?

4. Have you ever found yourself sneaking food? Why do you think you did it?

5. What do you think God thinks of your weight and your relationship with food?

6. Describe how it will feel when you are set free from your inappropriate relationship with food?

Chapter 2

1. How has this chapter changed the way you think about your relationship with food?

2. In what ways have you been "abused" by your relationship with food?

3. How have you ever made food the center of your day or the center of an event?

4. What have been some of the consequences of your inappropriate relationship with food?

5. In what ways have you tried to control the *consequences* of your inappropriate relationship with food instead of the relationship itself?

6. What did you learn about the origins of your eating problems by doing the timeline exercise?

7. Of the three "costs" described in this chapter, which one will be the most difficult for you to bear? Why? Which one will be the easiest and why?

8. What will your life be like if your relationship with food ends and how will you prepare yourself and others for your season of "raw" emotions?

Chapter 3

1. How has this chapter changed the way you think about your relationship with food?

2. In what ways have you taken God's provision of food for granted?

3. What means has God used to provide you with food today? Was there a store that provided a place to buy groceries? Did a friend take you out to eat?

4. What foods that you ate today can you sincerely be thankful for? Were there any foods or drinks that you could not be thankful for in good conscience?

5. What 'voices' in your life compete with the Holy Spirit in regard to food choices?

6. What will it be like for you to have the Holy Spirit guiding you on your eating decisions on a daily basis?

Chapter 4

1. How has this chapter changed the way you think about your relationship with food?

2. What conscious lies have you told about your eating?

3. What unconscious lies have you told about your eating?

4. Do you believe that *Spirit Led Eating* will work for you?

5. Who will be affected when you begin eating differently? How?

6. Looking in the mirror, what physical attribute can you be thankful for?

7. As you start applying *Spirit Led Eating* rule number 3, how will you feel if God chooses to "redeem your reflection?"

Chapter 5

1. In what ways are you picky about the foods you eat?

2. How have you complained about the food God and others have provided for you?

3. What consequences have you experienced due to complaining?

4. As you start applying *Spirit Led Eating* rule number 4, how will your lack of complaining about food positively affect others?

Chapter 6

1. How has this chapter changed the way you think about your relationship with food?

2. Have you ever thought of your eating behavior as "gluttonous" before? If so, why was it difficult for

you to acknowledge and turn away from this behavior?

3. How has shame been a factor in your overeating?

4. How has your inappropriate relationship with food
   made you feel as if you were on the "sidelines of
   God's will" for your life? Describe how that has affected you.

5. As you start applying *Spirit Led Eating* rule number
   5 and when you turn away from the sin of gluttony,
   in what ways do you want God to use you? What
   will you need to do to be used in this way(s)?

Chapter 7

1. How has this chapter changed the way you think
   about your relationship with food?

2. In what ways could you identify with the author's
   metaphor about taking his wife down a "bad road"
   through his overeating?

3. Take time to humbly ask others that you are close
   to how your overeating has negatively affected them.
   What were some of their responses?

4. How has your eating led others astray?

5. As you start applying *Spirit Led Eating* rule number
   6, how do you envision being able to positively influence people by the way you eat.

Chapter 8

1. How has this chapter changed the way you think about your relationship with food?

2. Do you have a secret stash of food that you withhold from others including your family? In light of what you are learning, what should you do with it?

3. What are some clever ways for you to provide food to others in need?

4. When you think of providing food for an enemy, what feelings are evoked?

5. As you start applying *Spirit Led Eating* rule number 7, how do you think sharing food with others will lead to greater freedom for you?

Chapter 9

1. How has this chapter changed the way you think about your relationship with food?

2. List some of the many things you can be thankful for.

3. How have you abused food when you have felt sad, lonely, or spiritually drained in the past?

4. How do you feel before celebrations in regard to your eating? Do you dread their arrival, do you sometimes look forward to an excuse to overeat, or a combination of both?

5. As you start applying *Spirit Led Eating* rule number 8, how will you be able to better enjoy the food God provides?

Chapter 10

1. Are you ready to "get well?" Did you make a positive choice to allow God to bring healing in your life through *Spirit Led Eating*? If so, what is different about this decision compared to other times you decided to lose weight or exercise more? If not, what is keeping you from letting go?

2. When you think of fasting, what do you envision? What steps do you need to take prior to entering into this spiritual discipline?

3. How can you become more vigilant when it comes to *Spirit Led Eating*?

4. List some of the people that you know who may be good candidates for joining you as you begin to walk in the truths of *Spirit Led Eating*? What steps do you need to take to enlist their support?

5. What are some activities and pursuits that you will have more time for when you stop thinking about and acting on your desires to overeat?

6. Looking back over the eight rules, which one or two do you think will be most difficult for you to live out? What steps do you need to take to gain confidence in these areas?

To order additional copies of

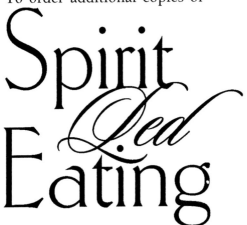

Spirit
Led
Eating

Have your credit card ready and call:

1-877-421-READ (7323)

or please visit our web site at
www.pleasantword.com

Also available at:
www.amazon.com
and
www.barnesandnoble.com

Printed in the United States
28128LVS00006B/37-45